CW00687720

WITH WINGS AS EAGLES

Aerial shot of the Queens Island site showing the Shorts Main Factory and surrounding production facilities

WITH WINGS AS EAGLES

Fifty years of Missile Manufacturing in Belfast

1952 – 2002

Eric Waugh

Corporate Document Services

© Thales Air Defence, 2003
© of photography Thales Air Defence, 2003
all rights reserved

©Eric Waugh, 2003
has asserted his rights under the
Copyright, Designs and Patents Act 1988 to be identified
as the author of this work.

Design by Corporate Document Services Limited, Belfast
Printed in Northern Ireland by W & G Baird Limited

A CIP catalogue record for this book
is available from the British Library

ISBN 1 84123 5636

They Shall Mount up with Wings as Eagles

Old Testament: Isaiah, xl,v31

Contents

Preface

THIS book, celebrating a half-century of achievement in one of the most advanced areas of precision engineering, tells a remarkable story. It is the tale of how something was built from nothing: something very considerable, giving birth to an organisation which, after a mere fifty years, has shown itself to be a world-beater in its chosen field; and winner of a long series of Queen's Awards for its innovating technology and its success in exporting it. I commend the story to the entrepreneurs of tomorrow as an example of what can be accomplished from small beginnings, provided there is the will to win.

In the circumstances most of it has never been told before. The technology of missile systems tends to be a secret science. Roger Bacon recorded a formula for gunpowder in 1260, but he wrote it in code to keep it from falling into the wrong hands. Missile designers and their fabricators are still the repository of many secrets – and for the same reason. But the veil is lifted here for the first time, sufficiently, I hope, to convey something of the excitement and the extent of the achievement involved.

It must be acknowledged at the outset that the armaments industry is not everyone's cup of tea. Many contemplate with mixed feelings its zeal in merchandising its deadly hardware round the world. Others openly harbour moral scruples. These reached their zenith in the late 1960s, in the early days of Castlereagh, when a particularly bitter jungle war in South-East Asia coincided with the arrival of colour television as a mass medium in the Western democracies. The fallout from the offloading of napalm canisters and agent orange by American helicopter gunships over North Vietnam and Cambodia between 1965 and 1973 was meat and drink to television news. It was the first colour television war. The critical viewpoint of its young radicals swelled the ranks of the anti-war lobby and, by extension, the critics of the armaments industry.

But there is another side to the argument and it tends to be overlooked by protesters. Throughout its life the resourceful scientists and engineers of Castlereagh have worked in a world free of global conflict. The peace may be armed – but in a world sense it has been kept: sometimes very narrowly, as in Berlin in 1948 and again in the Cuban missile standoff in 1962. Additionally, there have been regional conflicts, at times very savage; some of them feature in this story; terrorism remains an enveloping global threat in the new century; but – and this is most important to those of my generation who lived through the last one – there has been no world war.

The balance of power was a major element in keeping the peace in the generation which ended with the disintegration of the Soviet bloc in the years after 1989. The defensive close-range missiles, which comprise the special territory of Castlereagh, played their part in safeguarding the Western component of that balance. Every citizen lived a safer life as a result. It is the purpose of this story to acknowledge the notable contribution the people of the Castlereagh plant played in preserving that security.

This book has been written quickly amid the pull of other commitments and it could not have been done alone. Martin Armour was generous enough to let me have the typescript of his autobiography before its recent publication. My account of the early years could not have been written without it. George Jackson, who first proposed that this book should be written, similarly and with equal generosity, let me have a copy of the typescript of the completed portion of his own memoir of the earlier years. I talked at length to both of them and Jackson has read the text and saved me from numerous technical errors therein. I am also indebted to David Beatty, Millar Crawford, Lindsay Cumming, Sir Philip Foreman, Maurice McFadden, John Potts, Terry Stone and George Townend. John Leighton spared an afternoon to give me a close-up tour of his marvellous state of the art plant at Castlereagh. All were ungrudging of their time. Andy Lyttle has been an assiduous and exhaustive picture editor, trawling an extensive archive, which reveals the expansive range of the Precision Engineering Department's early activities. He also made available to me a voluminous file of Shorts' history. All these lines seemed to end up on Denise Clarke's desk. She has been indispensable in organising liaison, arranging meetings, fixing appointments and seeking to ensure that I kept to the schedule. Elsewhere, Niall Sherry of the *Belfast Telegraph* library has been a most valuable guide within that mine of information. The efficient staff of the Linenhall Library in Belfast have produced vital reference volumes without fail. To my wife I say thank you for enduring the months of silence, when the study door remained shut all day every day, for refraining from grumbling and for being so ready with encouragement.

Eric Waugh

County Down
March 2003

SHORTS COMES TO BELFAST

W HEN the surrendered warships of the German Grand
Fleet were scuttled by their crews at Scapa Flow after the
end of the First World War, almost every vessel salvaged
was found to have been fitted with the great ventilating fans
manufactured by Davidson & Company in Belfast. Half a century
earlier, the members of the Musgrave family of Belfast were producing
their top-of-the-range stable fittings in cast iron. Their clients
eventually included most of the crowned heads of Europe, including
the German Emperor, the Spanish Queen, the King of the
Netherlands, not to mention the Prince of Wales, later King Edward
VII, and notable engineers of the day like Friedrich Krupp of Essen and
Alexandre-Gustave Eiffel of Paris. The Falls Foundry in west Belfast
manufactured shells for the Artillery in the Crimea and sharpened the
sabres of the Inniskilling Dragoons who fought at Balaclava.[1]

Engineering was an unlikely growth in Ulster. There was no
appreciable ore; above all, no material coal seams. Unsurprisingly, the
industry was largely an imported phenomenon. It prospered because
the people proved that, in spite of the lack of indigenous raw
materials, they could do it. Shipbuilding is a celebrated part of the
story, reaching its apotheosis in International Mercantile Marine, the
powerful syndicate put together in 1902 by William Pirrie, J. Pierpoint
Morgan and J. Bruce Ismay. Significantly, it was Pirrie, the former
Belfast shipyard apprentice, who was the moving spirit. He was to
build the liners at Harland & Wolff; Morgan, through his New York
banking connections, was to raise the finance; and Ismay, of the White
Star Line, was to operate them. The rest is history, as evidenced by
the epic tale of the three sisters, *Olympic, Titanic* and *Britannic*, the first
two being ordered in 1907 at a cost, immense for the time, of more
than £3m.[2]

At the same time (actually on New Year's Eve, 1909) in a field near
the village of Hillsborough, County Down, an enterprising young
engineer, a farmer's son of 25, became the first man to fly in Ireland.
His name was Harry Ferguson and he used a monoplane designed and
built by himself. His interest in aviation followed the successful design,
building and racing of his own motor cycle and car. Lilian Bland of

Carnmoney, County Antrim built and flew her own biplane, quizzically named *Mayfly*, at Randalstown in the summer of 1910, establishing a claim to have been the first woman to build and fly her own aircraft.[3]

During the First World War Harland & Wolff built aircraft for both de Havilland and Avro. In 1918 they collaborated with Handley Page in producing V1500 heavy bombers, largest of the day and intended for use in retaliatory raids on Berlin. The 170 acres of Aldergrove Farm in south Antrim were bought to provide a base for the aircraft. But the end of the war killed the contract prematurely when only four had been built.[4]

Following the accession of Hitler to the German chancellorship with dictatorial powers in 1933, the Government had been concerned at the progress of German rearmament. The German Air Force, proscribed in the 1919 peace settlement at Versailles, was officially, if secretly, reborn on 26 February 1935 under Hermann Goering as Commander-in-Chief, with nearly 2,000 aircraft and 20,000 men. On 4 March the British defence white paper pointedly referred to the peril of German rearmament. This appears to have nettled Hitler. He at once arranged an exclusive interview with G. Ward Price of the *Daily Mail* in the course of which the rebirth of the Luftwaffe, widely suspected, was admitted officially for the first time. A week later Hitler denounced the Versailles settlement, announcing that the Nazis planned to introduce conscription and raise an army of 36 divisions (about 550,000 men).[5]

At the end of the month, the Foreign Secretary, Sir John Simon, accompanied by his Minister of State (and eventual successor), Anthony Eden, went to Berlin for arms talks with Hitler. It proved a correct, but cool and unproductive, series of meetings. The shock came towards the close, after an argument over the strength of the air forces of Britain and France. Simon asked Hitler point blank what was the current strength of the Luftwaffe. Hitler announced that Germany had already reached parity with Great Britain. Asked about an air pact, Hitler said he would consider one only if it excluded any limitation on the size of the air forces.

For the British this rather destroyed the point. The result of the Berlin talks was to alarm ministers sufficiently to propel them at once into a radical revision of the RAF expansion programme. This had been approved only in the preceding July. It provided for a home air force of 84 squadrons by March 1939, and even that plan had been attacked by its opponents as a panic measure. However, with the endorsement of a decisive general election victory in November 1935, Stanley Baldwin moved at once to respond to the German resurgence. In the defence white paper of February 1936 the RAF was to have a home strength of 124 squadrons, not 84.

Within a few months, plans began to take detailed form. One such was the issue of Specification B.12/36 in July for a high-speed long-range heavy bomber, the first step towards the birth of the aircraft which, was to be the RAF's first four-engined strike weapon[6]. Another key detail was the stipulation by the RAF that shadow factories would be essential if the new aircraft production targets were to be met. This was unanswerable and the defence requirements committee accepted it at the end of 1935 when it urged the creation of a shadow armaments industry. The Government would build (and pay for) the factories; but they would be run by existing firms.[7] Furthermore, they would be as far north-west of London as was practicable.

In the straitened circumstances of the inter-war years in Belfast, manufacturers never lost sight of the commercial potential of the armaments industry. Sir Frederick Rebbeck, who took charge of the affairs of Harland & Wolff as sole Managing Director in 1930, was particularly active in pushing ahead secret negotiations with the War Office, the Admiralty and the Air Ministry. Munitions work had one signal advantage over civil: as well as producing profit and employment, it was likely to involve investment of substantial Government funds in new purpose-built factories.

Rebbeck, knowing he had the backing of the Northern Ireland Government, made arrangements for an Air Ministry official to look over the facilities at Harland & Wolff which had been used to build aircraft in the later stages of the First World War. His visitor expressed satisfaction with what he saw, but when he reported accordingly, the Air Ministry came under pressure from existing aircraft builders anxious to hold on to the lucrative RAF contracts for themselves. Rebbeck, acting on the basis of the tested slogan that, if you cannot beat them, join them, proceeded to open negotiations on his own account with aircraft builders in the south-east of England. He baited his hook with the lure that he was willing to consider a new company, jointly owned.

Rebbeck's negotiations began to accelerate when he discovered that Short Brothers of Rochester were embarrassed by an order book they could not accommodate at their Kent base. They anticipated gaining business from the rearmament programme; and they had laid down the first aircraft production line world-wide; but they were well aware that they had not the space to undertake large-scale production of their *Sunderland* flying boats for the RAF. They were also aware that in Belfast there was a labour force waiting, and a site with the necessary open access to the waters of Belfast Lough with the bonus of a deep-water berth where aircraft carriers could, if necessary, load and unload aeroplanes. By April 1936, Rebbeck had drawn up heads of agreement with Short Brothers to build aircraft at Belfast.

In fact Shorts was not to be responsible for the new factory. In a foretaste of the future which none could then anticipate, under Rebbeck's deal, the Air Ministry was to build and equip it. The management would be in the hands of a new company, Short & Harland Limited, in which the Air Ministry stipulated Short Brothers was to have a controlling interest. In the event the new Company was registered in June with Shorts holding 60 per cent. and Harland & Wolff the remainder.[8]

The new plant began producing the first components at the end of Belfast's traditional July holiday shutdown in 1937. Its first contracts were for 50 Bristol *Bombay* transports followed by 150 already ageing twin-engined Handley Page *Hereford* bombers.

ROCHESTER AIRFIELD

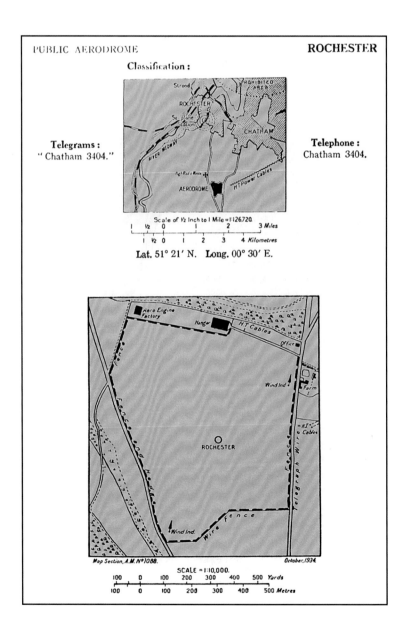

NOTES

1   W.E. Coe: *The Engineering Industry in the North of Ireland* (Newton Abbot, 1969) pp 114, 121-2

2   Michael Moss and John R. Hume: *Shipbuilders to the World* (Belfast, 1986) pp108, 138

3   *The Concise Dictionary of National Biography*, vol 1 (Oxford, 1995) p 986; Coe, op.cit., p 105

4   Moss & Hume, op.cit., pp199-200

5   John Terraine: *The Right of the Line* (London, 1985) pp 31-2

6   C.H. Barnes: *Shorts Aircraft since 1900* (London, 1967) p 370; Terraine, op.cit., p34

7   Terraine, op.cit., pp 35-6

8   Moss & Hume, op.cit. pp 307-8; Barnes, op.cit., pp 27-8

2

STRESSES OF WAR

THE build-up proceeded at an accelerating pace in step with the ominous course events were taking on continental Europe. As war approached, both the shipyard and the new aircraft factory in Belfast were equipped for substantial fabrication of military aeroplanes. The new Shorts facility provided space for sub-assemblies, final assembly line and a lofty flight shed, so that the aircraft could be processed, like motor cars, on the latest flow system, with the convenience of the airfield for subsequent engine running-up and flight tests being a major bonus.[1] In the meantime, three months before Neville Chamberlain's fateful flight to Munich in September 1938, Rebbeck concluded an agreement with the War Office under which it was to fit out an armaments plant within Harland & Wolff at a cost of £250,000.[2]

The need for a civil airport for the Belfast region had been widely discussed during the 1930s. A number of locations had been considered, including nearby Newtownards and the southern edge of the city. But the Harbour Commissioners had been pushing ahead an ambitious land reclamation programme on the eastern side of the port. It was the potential of this, coupled with the nascent plan for the aircraft factory, which, early in 1936, fixed the choice on Sydenham. The launching in the city of a unit of the RAF Volunteer Reserve, with its need for flying facilities near at hand, was also influential.[3] In the event the new Belfast Harbour Airport was cleared for public use by the Air Ministry in September 1937. In May 1938, an increasingly air-minded Government exploited it to stage an Empire Air Day pageant. A large crowd of civilian spectators watched antique biplanes make simulated bombing runs, dropping smoke bombs on a mock-up of buildings on the airfield. The antiquity, of course, was relative: some of the RAF's biplanes, amazingly, were very new, the Gloster *Gladiator* having only entered RAF service 17 months before. But it was to be the last. In hindsight, bearing in mind the dreadful fate of the city of Belfast almost precisely three years ahead, the irony of the occasion was bitter. But the antiquity of the aeroplanes' design, little different in their externals from those which dived and wove above the trenches on the Western Front in 1918, served to underline for the professionals how grievous was the need for the new manufacture in which Belfast was now to play a part. In fact, just a year later, the first aircraft to be produced by Short & Harland's new factory took off from the Sydenham runway on its delivery flight. Symbolically it was a monoplane, a twin-engined Bristol *Bombay* military transport and night bomber. It was April 1939 and Short & Harland in that year already had a payroll of 8,451. The size of the labour force in Harland & Wolff devoted to aircraft output is unknown, but the total employment at Belfast had reached 17,850 by the end of 1939. The shipbuilding base of the group in Belfast, swollen by wartime needs, was to reach a peak labour force of 30,801 in 1944.

Shorts had tendered for the Air Ministry's specification B.12/36, issued in July 1936, described as a high-speed, long range, four-engined, strategic bomber with a crew of six sharing nine functions. The company succeeded in having its design selected, along with that put in by Supermarine. Each company was to build two prototypes.[4] In fact, as intelligence reports indicated continuing increases in the size of the Luftwaffe, the first order for 100 of its design was placed with Shorts in Rochester even before the prototype had flown. In April 1938 the Wehrmacht marched into Austria, which resulted in a doubling of the order, with the contract for a second 100 being placed with Short & Harland in Belfast. The aircraft, a technical trailblazer for those which came after, was named the *Stirling*. The first entered RAF service in August 1940. The chequered and exciting story of the great aircraft during the Second World War has been told elsewhere. Suffice it to say that, by the middle of 1945, with the war in Europe over, 236 had been built at Belfast. Overtaken as heavy bombers by the *Halifax* and the *Lancaster*, the successors profited from the lessons taught by Shorts pioneering design. But *Stirlings* continued in service as troop transports, as glider tugs on D-Day in June 1944, at Arnhem and Nijmegen three months later and in the final assault across the Rhine in March 1945. *Stirlings* were also used by the special squadrons which dropped arms and supplies to the *Maquis* in occupied France and the Resistance in Belgium in 1943 and 1944.

The *Sunderland* flying boat, of which more than 700 were built at Rochester, Dumbarton and Belfast, also made a signal contribution to the war effort. Its most vital role was with RAF Coastal Command, providing long-range air cover for merchant convoys during the Battle of the Atlantic. A considered view is that it could not have been won without it.[5] In that event, the issue of the Second World War itself would have been put in doubt.

The stresses inseparable from wartime production brought inter-personal problems as well. Shorts was still a company in private ownership, but with the inherent embarrassment of having effectively only one customer, the Government. At the head of that

Government, a wartime coalition of three parties, was a Prime Minister with autocratic powers which gave him total dominance. Most of the work Shorts was doing was highly secret. Government officials exploited the exigencies of the hour to convey the message that the war effort demanded total obedience. In this situation, if differences of opinion over policy occurred, a private company's hands would be tied. The censor muzzled the newspapers, the cinema newsreels, and the wireless. The issues in dispute could not be discussed in public because they hinged upon matters which were secret. So it was against this background that, in January 1943, Sir Stafford Cripps, Minister of Aircraft Production, made it clear to Oswald Short, last in office of the Short brothers, that he must step down from the chairmanship.

Short, at the age of 60, had been running the company virtually on his own for 25 years, since his brother, Horace, had died in 1917. But like many entrepreneurs of initiative and drive, he was poor at delegating, did not suffer fools gladly and could be impatient. As a result he had made enemies among the officials of the Air Ministry and the Ministry of Aircraft Production.[6] In fact the strain of the vast production load imposed upon the company by the Government, coupled with the unpredictable policy changes which accompanied changes of Minister, were bound to exacerbate these traits.

Short remained on the boards of both companies in Rochester and Belfast, but he was succeeded as Chairman by the head of the Thomas Tilling transport group, Sir Frederick Heaton. When further changes were initiated by Heaton upon which the board had not been consulted, including the appointment of an unknown Thomas Tilling colleague as Managing Director, it declined to approve them. This led to further friction with the Government which in March brought in an accountant, Kenneth Layton Bennett, as Controller. A week later, without warning, Cripps used his powers under the wartime defence regulations to expropriate all the shares. In April, again without consultation, he made sweeping changes on the board, removing the directors with longest service, including Oswald Short himself. It was, as the company's historian records, "a swift and utterly ruthless Government take-over that deeply upset Oswald and the other directors, and severely shook the morale of the work-force".[7] The atmosphere was not helped by Cripps' refusal to give any undertaking that the expropriated shares would be restored to their owners after the war or compensation paid. Questioned in the Commons, the Minister declined to enlarge on the reasons for his action, beyond stating that it was necessary for the "effective control of the undertaking".

This episode was important for the future history of the company if only because it left a bad taste in the mouth of the Shorts' management which, over the years, it proved difficult to remove. It began an argument over the official treatment of the enterprise by Government which only ended when it was returned to commercial ownership in 1989. The implication on the official side that the company was inefficient was bitterly rejected by its senior personnel. Official criticism of the unit cost of the *Stirlings* and their rate of production was thrown back at the official side with a reminder that orders placed for it had been too small and materials essential for the aircraft robbed of top priority in 1942 and, being unavailable when needed, unavoidably delayed output.[8]

In fact the company had been rather brutally pitchforked into a new world where a national Government was coping, day to day, with a running emergency where a high degree of desperation was the ruling norm. Two generations later, with contemporary papers and memoirs available, it is clear the extent to which official policy in wartime was being made on the hoof and how improvisation was relied upon continuously as an essential device. For Government there was no alternative. Survival was the name of the national game.

For Shorts, however, it was stiff medicine. The company had to master the disciplines of mass production under the stress of war. Oswald Short retired bitterly to the wings, excluded from the game to which he was devoted and receiving no acknowledgement whatsoever from Government for a lifetime of signal services rendered.

NOTES

1 John W. Blake: *Northern Ireland in the Second World War* (Belfast 2000) p53

2 Moss & Hume, op.cit., p328

3 Blake, op.cit., p 52

4 Barnes, op.cit., p 370

5 Michael Donne: *Pioneers of the Skies* (Belfast, 1987) p 98

6 Donne, op.cit., p 99

7 Donne, op.cit., pp 99-101

8 Donne, op.cit., pp 104-5

3

CASTLEREAGH IS BORN

W HEN the Second World War ended in August 1945 with the fearful drama of the two nuclear strikes at Hiroshima and Nagasaki, the message they conveyed about the future was unmistakable. It was going to be a very different world from the effete and now distant 1930s. Peace was back: but the nuclear incineration of the two Japanese cities warned that, with the opposing blocs in possession of such destructive power, it would be an armed peace. Within three years the wartime allies narrowly avoided coming to blows over the Soviet blockade of Berlin. Two years after that, the rivals in the Cold War poured their armaments and men into a very hot one in Korea - on opposing sides.

For Shorts all this meant two things. In peacetime, wartime armaments budgets would be cut; and, as part of that process, the swollen aviation industry would contract. But there would still be a market for economically attractive weaponry: both the Berlin airlift and the Korean War served to stem the cutbacks in defence which had begun in 1945. The company, though, faced problems of its own. Its base at Rochester, dating back to the First World War, was unsuitable for further development. It was constricted by its surroundings and had poor transport links. In 1946 the decision was made to close it and to consolidate operations at Belfast. While this was a hard-nosed, practical move, it was not good for morale. The Government announcement, bound to be unpopular in the vote-rich home counties, typically was delegated by the Minister to the lowly lips of a Parliamentary Secretary. It stressed the need to cut the industry down to peacetime size. But, said the statement, the move had the advantage that at Shorts' Belfast plant there was room for expansion.[1] The logic of this reasoning was puzzling. It pointed to an uncertain future. In the event many of the most experienced employees in Kent chose not to move to Northern Ireland and took early retirement. The prevalent atmosphere of a change in direction was encouraged by corporate and financial adjustments out of which the reorganised group emerged in 1947 with the new name of Short Brothers & Harland Limited.

Thales Air Defence from the Air

The original Research and
Development facility at Castlereagh

In Belfast the late 1940s and 1950s were lean years. Shorts survived largely by building other people's aircraft: the English Electric *Canberra* light bomber, the Bristol *Britannia*, even briefly the de Havilland *Comet*. It also maintained a busy research and development programme. But it was clear that broader diversification was essential to safeguard the future of the company. Out of this conviction was born the Precision Engineering Division, the idea of the then Chairman, Rear Admiral Matthew Slattery.

Slattery, a naval aviation expert, had joined the Royal Navy as a cadet in 1916 and during the Second World War, after a command at sea, had come ashore as Director General of naval aircraft development at the Ministry of Aircraft Production. He joined Shorts as Managing Director on retirement from the Royal Navy in 1948. Four years later he also assumed the chairmanship of the company and was knighted in 1955.

Slattery had been at the coal face of the aviation business. He knew the business of Government procurement from the inside, its short-termism, its vulnerability to general elections and to ministerial change. In the late 1950s, while still with Shorts, he was a confidential adviser to the Prime Minister, Harold Macmillan. From this vantage point, he was convinced that, in the new post-war world, the company could not rely for its future on building aircraft alone. His hunch appeared to be only too accurate when the defence white paper of 1957 recommended drastic reductions in expenditure on RAF and naval aircraft, with the implication that many of their functions in future would be fulfilled by guided weapons.

Five years before, in 1952, the year he took over the chairmanship, Slattery had presided over the birth of Shorts, Castlereagh or, as it was officially known, the Precision Engineering Division. The new outfit was housed in a building erected as part of the local contribution to the Festival of Britain in 1951. The Festival represented a spirited bid to lift the exhausted nation out of the austere social and economic anti-climax of the immediate post-war years, with their acute rationing, shortages and draconian foreign exchange controls. As such, the use of this particular plant by Shorts was suitably symbolic: for the purpose of the venture was to release the company from its wartime role of near-total reliance on aircraft. To that end the new branch had an engineering department, another for research and a third for manufacturing.

The initiative was warmly supported by the Northern Ireland Ministry of Commerce, then flexing its post-war muscles with the aid of its innovating machinery of development grants. Shorts' new venture was precisely the sort of activity the Ministry was keen to encourage. It was aware that the new facility would offer employment to the young engineering graduates who would soon be issuing from the technical colleges and Queen's University in increasing numbers, the result of the Northern Ireland Education Act of 1947. This replicated the Butler Act passed by the Commons at Westminster three years before, opening the way to grant-aided places in further education for the first time.

The Northern Ireland Government was also keenly interested in the potential of Shorts' new venture because it would require specialised engineering skills on the shop floor for which there had, until then, been little outlet in Northern Ireland. Finally, the labour-intensive finished products would be high-value items of modest bulk compared to the output of Ulster's traditional heavy engineering industry and therefore not difficult or inordinately expensive to transport to the market.

The research department promptly identified the growing application of electronics to industrial processes as an area of potential. The computers at the National Physical Laboratory and in university departments in Great Britain were booked up months ahead by Government departments and industrial firms. Shorts were soon manufacturing the first general purpose analogue computer to be put into quantity production in the British Isles. There had been others: but they had been special-purpose instruments, designed to order and priced out of reach of many potential users. By contrast, Shorts' instrument was an off-the-shelf device designed for cost-effective series production. The prototype, in fact, starting from scratch, had been designed and built in a mere eight months.

Because it was capable of dealing with physical quantities which vary continuously, such as current or voltage, it had an application to

The first production line of analogue computers in the British Isles

the aircraft industry. In fact it was the need for it by the company's aircraft designers, and the reluctance of Shorts to spend scarce dollars buying one from the United States, that drove them to design their own. The device, indeed, could be used to solve the equations involved in calculating aircraft stability and vibration. It also had an application in the design of automatic pilots for both missiles and aircraft.

With the aid of a cockpit and a set of instruments and controls, the computer could be set to respond to a test pilot's manoeuvres in the manner of the real aircraft. It was then a novelty but in essence corresponded to what every civil airline pilot on a familiarisation course with a new aircraft now calls a simulator. The big breakthrough for the designer was that, although his aircraft might exist only on paper or the computer screen, he could now be aware of its promised performance.

Shorts' analogue computer made its first appearance at the Royal Aircraft Establishment show at Farnborough in Hampshire in 1953, where it won its first orders. Others soon followed from both industry and Government. One of the foreign orders was from the Dutch Aeronautical Institute at Amsterdam.

At the planning stage Shorts had engaged an experienced consultant, Reuben Hedekel, to advise on the sales potential of their new product. He delivered a report identifying sectors of the engineering industry and certain of the big public authorities as the

Analogue computers being used in calculating aircraft stability and vibration

prime targets. In fact his prediction that the company could hope to sell seventy was amazingly accurate. Eventual sales were seventy-two. The computer sold at £5,300, a large sum in the mid-1950s, when the average British wage-earner received only £500 a year and the salaried employee £760. Typical customers were precisely those Hedekel had forecast: the nuclear power industry, engineering establishments, technical colleges and, of course, aircraft manufacturers.

Assembling the essential technical staff at Castlereagh involved careful planning. The research department of the Precision Engineering Division was the only entity in Northern Ireland providing work on electronic and precision instruments for engineering graduates. Because engineers with specialised experience were required at the outset, senior jobs had to be filled from outside the province. But in 1955, within three years of the launching of Castlereagh, Shorts' Chief Research Engineer, Lloyd Thomas, recruited some time before from Sperry Rand, already had a staff of sixty. Many had been trained within the new Castlereagh works, with the accent on youth. Soon talks were going on with the regional Ministry of Commerce about a new building comprising three floors, capable of accommodating up to 300 staff for the research department.

One or two individual cases indicate how the necessary skills were assembled. Bob Paul, a young man from the north Antrim resort of Portrush, went from Coleraine Technical School to Queens University in Belfast and thence to the University of London. He studied at

The programme for the opening of the Research Building, built to meet the expanding requirements of the overall company.

Battersea Polytechnic, taking an honours degree. After graduation he worked for the Motor Industries Research Association. He returned to Northern Ireland in 1952 and shortly afterwards was appointed head of the Electronics Research Department.

Maurice McFadden from Bushmills, County Antrim, home of the celebrated village distillery half a dozen miles east of Portrush, took an electrical engineering degree at Queen's University in 1950 and, after post-graduate studies in radio, was recruited as a development engineer at Castlereagh in 1953. Martin Armour of Ballyclare, in the Antrim countryside north of Belfast, was another recruit from Queen's University, joining Shorts soon after the opening of the Belfast factory in 1936. Later he was to join the Ministry of Supply to work, first on radar, and then on atomic weapons. He was to return to Shorts as a project engineer at Castlereagh.

The plant was also to play its part as a training base for the company's other production lines. An apprentice training school was opened at Castlereagh in 1953 and competition for places was intense. In 1954 there were 1,500 applicants from schools in the United Kingdom and Commonwealth countries for only 200 available places.

In retrospect it is not difficult to divine why. In addition to the computer project and the aircraft design and production at Queen's Island, Shorts' Castlereagh plant was also involved with micro-engineering at a sophisticated level. Electric motors only an inch in diameter were being developed. A newspaper of the time referred to these as being "for airborne apparatus" or for "classified projects which may not be mentioned at present"[2]. Little by little, the intriguing shape which the future of Castlereagh was to take was being revealed.

In the meantime the computer venture was to accelerate as a direct result of the demands of the aircraft side in the main Shorts plant at Queen's Island. A proposal from the company to build a research aircraft to confront the problems of vertical take-off and landing had resulted in a Government contract for two. Design work on the SC1 research aircraft began in 1952. It was to be the first VTOL fixed-wing aeroplane built in the United Kingdom. The delta-winged craft used five Rolls Royce jet engines: four for vertical take-off and a fifth for forward propulsion. The revolutionary beast was taken on board ship at Belfast and thence by road to the Government

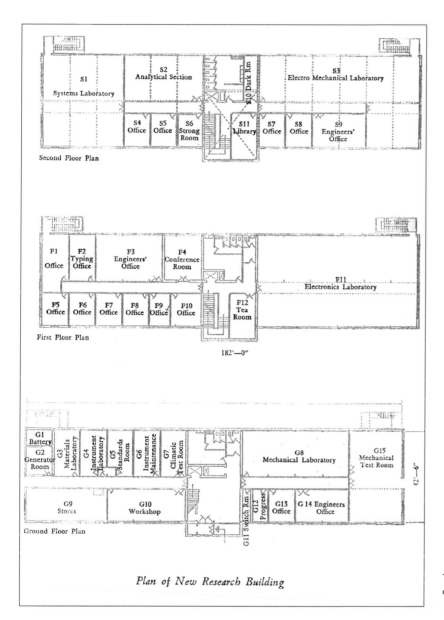

Second Floor Plan

S1	S2		S3
Systems Laboratory	Analytical Section	S10 Dark Rm	Electro Mechanical Laboratory

	S4 Office	S5 Office	S6 Strong Room	S11 Library	S7 Office	S8 Office	S9 Engineers' Office

First Floor Plan

F1 Office	F2 Typing Office	F3 Engineers' Office	F4 Conference Room	F11 Electronics Laboratory
F5 Office	F6 Office	F7 Office	F8 Office	F9 Office	F10 Office	F12 Tea Room	

182'—0"

Ground Floor Plan

G1 Battery
G2 Generator Room
G3 Materials Laboratory
G4 Instrument Laboratory
G5 Standards Room
G6 Instrument Maintenance
G7 Climatic Test Room
G8 Mechanical Laboratory
G15 Mechanical Test Room

G9 Stores
G10 Workshop
G11 Switch Rm
G12 Progress
G13 Office
G14 Engineers Office

42'—6"

Plan of New Research Building

The plan showing the layout of the building

Experimental Establishment at Boscombe Down in Wiltshire in March 1957. On 2 April it made its first flight. A year later the second aircraft demonstrated both vertical take-off and hovering.

For Castlereagh the importance of the SC1 lay in its requirement of an entirely new range of electronic flight controls and controls for its complex hydraulic systems. Castlereagh, of course, had no design engineers with the necessary experience. But, as Martin Armour recalls, "there was the electronics department all ready to go". In addition the mechanical engineering department had an ex-naval officer with wide experience of warships' electro-hydraulic weapons systems. In fact it was the young engineers' knowledge of computing techniques, exploited in the use of their own analogue product, which enabled the research team effectively to fly the SCI inside the department. There was, as yet, no moving platform to reproduce the changing attitude of the flight deck, as used later to train airline pilots. But the computer otherwise simulated flying conditions with the cockpit instruments revealing how the aircraft would react. It was at this stage that an important new door was opened through which a fresh wind of new thinking began to blow.

The Autostabilisation Gyroscope developed for the SCI Vertical Take Off and Land (VTOL) aircraft

Computers used to simulate the flight of the SC1 aircraft

___

NOTES

1   Donne, op.cit., pp 115-6

2   *Belfast Telegraph*, 15 April 1955

4

LEADING FROM THE FRONT

I n 1954 Hugh Graham Conway was a 40-year-old vintage motoring enthusiast whose special love was that French classic, the Bugatti. Born in Vancouver, British Columbia, he went to school in Edinburgh and then to Cambridge. His first knowledge of Northern Ireland was probably absorbed from a fellow-student, the young Dennis Rebbeck, whose father was the Chairman of Harland & Wolff and a member of Shorts' board. Conway had joined the aircraft industry at the age of 24 on leaving Cambridge in 1938 and was soon marked out as an engineer of promise. He spent the war years with Aircraft Equipment Limited, moved on to the aviation division of Dunlop Rubber and, in 1947, to the British subsidiary of the French Messier concern in Gloucestershire, where as a technical director, he became an expert on the design of landing gear. But, in maturity, he had developed another striking attribute upon which Matthew Slattery fastened at once: he was a born innovator and a dynamic personality almost to the point of flamboyance. To Conway, every problem was a challenge; and the more abstruse the problem, the more taunting the challenge. Slattery decided at once that he must have Conway as his chosen instrument, both to lighten his mounting burden at Shorts and to chart the company's future.[1] His first injunction to the new Chief Engineer was to give free rein to his innovating talents and to build up the Precision Engineering Division as a new and major pillar of the company.

Conway was to admit later that this was not such a shot in the dark as might have been supposed. "We knew," he said, "of an interest in the Navy in a low-cost missile to replace the Bofors gun."[2] This was a tempting commercial prospect. Bofors was the leader worldwide in its artillery field. Its 40mm light artillery piece was probably the most successful design of its kind ever produced - and is still in use. From the start, when in 1928 the Swedish Navy issued its requirement to A. B. Bofors, it had been conceived as a ship-to-air weapon, although it later also became famous in a ground-to-air role. With its shell of just under 2lb., propelled at an impressive muzzle velocity of 2,802 feet per second, it could bring down any aircraft it hit. By the mid 1920s the

Opposite: HG Conway (right) supported by the Company Chairman, Rear Admiral Sir Matthew Slattery (left) hosting personnel from Naval Construction

Bofors works in the Baltic port of Karlskrona in south-east Sweden had a formidable order book. In addition it had made licence agreements for the production of both gun and ammunition with manufacturers all over Europe, all of which were fully operational by 1939. In the event, although the Swedish firm was domiciled in a non-combatant nation in the Second World War, its contribution was to prove crucial – on both sides. Licence agreements with Bofors had been employed by the Germans in their first attempts to circumvent the punitive limitations on rearmament imposed by the Treaty of Versailles in 1919. The Swedes accordingly co-operated with Krupp as early as the 1920s in the development of the 88mm anti-aircraft anti-tank gun. As a result, when the Nazis took office in 1933, these fully-fledged clandestine operations were shown to have reached an advanced stage. In fact the first models of the new "88" were delivered to the Wehrmacht in 1934 and, only two years later, astounded military observers worldwide when their performance was revealed by Franco's troops in the Spanish Civil War.[3]

Shorts' interest in the replacement for the 40mm Bofors was soundly based because it had become almost the standard anti-aircraft armament for naval vessels. It was also a sophisticated weapon, capable of delivering up to 120 rounds a minute. It used a clip-fed system and the firing sequence was automatic once the trigger was pressed. Castlereagh was still in its infancy and sustained by a largely youthful staff; but, undaunted, it had chosen an ambitious niche of high prestige to fill.

"H. G." or more irreverently, "Big Hugh", as the new Chief Engineer soon became known, was to provide a notable motive force. Conway had a broad engineering experience in all its applications from design to production. He had written widely in the professional journals on the secret of successful assembly of components provided by different sub-contractors. He was known throughout the industry as an expert on "limits and fits": how to ensure that two parts made by two different people would, when brought together, fit without time-wasting adjustment. As he walked down the aisle of the drawing office at Castlereagh, stopping to talk to a draughtsman, he could look at the drawing and at once visualise its subject in three dimensions.[4] In addition, he was physically impressive: over six feet tall, with a mop of wavy, very fair hair. In fact, as George Jackson, later Resident Engineer in some of Shorts most successful missile markets overseas, recalled, Conway was a dynamic character who bestrode the division. "The swing doors at the front office hadn't stopped swinging when he walked down the drawing office--which was on the next floor. Initially we didn't have a directional drive: then H. G. appeared on the scene."[5] But the new department was still without a product capable of promising a long-term commercial future. Without it, it was recognised that even the new Chief Engineer would find it difficult to

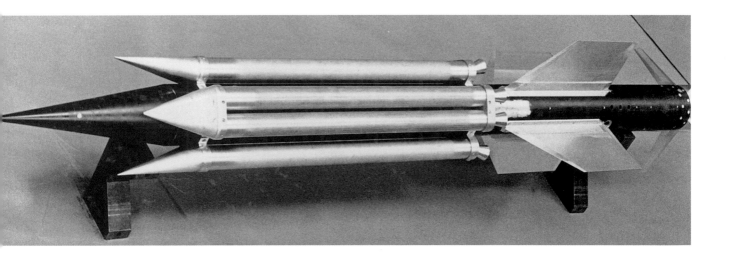

maintain the momentum essential for survival.

Conway was attracted to guided weapons for three reasons. The first was the clear commercial potential. The second was that he had already had experience of working with rocket motors. The third was that the Precision Engineering Department already had a contract from the Royal Aircraft Establishment at Farnborough.

The RAE had set up a guided weapons department during the 1940s. After the war its staff pursued research in conjunction with the Rocket Propulsion Establishment at Westcott near Oxford. The RPE was investigating rocket motors using both solid and liquid propellants. For the flight trials they were using the hardware left over from an abandoned wartime naval missile venture, naming the project RTV1. But, realising its limitations, they were co-operating with Folland Aircraft in the search for a replacement. Although the work had reached an advanced stage, it was abandoned in favour of handing over the design and building task to Shorts' newly-formed Precision Engineering Department at Castlereagh. The RAE retained overall design authority, but Castlereagh had won possession of its first venture into the guided missile field. The new creation, given the uninspiring label of General Purpose Vehicle, was at once dubbed the GPV. Its slim cylindrical fuselage, 27 feet long with a wing span of five feet, bore within it the future hopes of the new missile division.

The plan was to use the supersonic GPV to test a wide range of components: guidance and control systems, instrumentation and liquid and solid-propellant motors, not forgetting the vital matter of the telemetry, the means by which instrument readings on the test vehicle in flight were fed back to the firing point by radio. Accordingly, the engineers from Castlereagh were seconded to both the RAE and RPE to study the new techniques.

Because Conway was very much a hands-on manager, he became deeply involved with the guided weapons department at the RAE.

The General Purpose Vehicle (GPV), with jettisonable motors, used to test propulsion systems and guidance and control systems.

23

The GPV in production

Where, with a less extrovert visiting executive, relationships might have been restricted by formality, in H.G.'s case they flourished. It was no liability that the then Head of Guided Weapons at the RAE, W.H. Stevens, had been born and educated in Northern Ireland. One vital result was that Conway was soon privy to the nature and detail of the RAE's advance planning and able to assess its potential for Shorts. He learned that the armed services were co-operatively exploring how to improve high level anti-aircraft defence, but there was also much discussion on the future of short-range weapons: anti-tank for the Army and close-range defence for the Navy – the replacement for the 40mm Bofors gun.

This, indeed, for Shorts was the key requirement. Conway took due note that, because the re-equipment order would be so wholesale, a premium would be placed on a cheap and comparatively simple, cost-effective system. In fact the RAE took their cue from the pioneer work done by the Germans in the late stages of the Second World War, when the Wehrmacht had used manually-guided anti-tank weapons with much success. But to design a similar device, one which could be used on the rolling deck of a warship at speed, to despatch a warhead accurately at a diving or weaving jet aircraft, would be quite something else. In effect Shorts' work on the GPV, which seemed, like so many similar research contracts, to lead nowhere commercially, was to provide the sorely-needed gateway to the commercial future. Conway was convinced that the future lay with guided weapons. He was determined Shorts would not be left out.

But Castlereagh confronted the challenge of the GPV with marked liabilities on board. Shorts was one of the last of the aircraft manufacturers to become seriously involved with guided weapons. When the design team was formed at Castlereagh in 1952, it was made up of aircraft engineers from the aircraft factory at Queen' s Island supplemented by a small number of new recruits. None of them had experience of guided weapons. The same applied to the manufacturing team. But, in the words of George Jackson, "What they lacked in experience they made up for in enthusiasm."[7]

In the meantime RAE were building a vast simulator which represented a new advance on the frontiers of computer control. As Martin Armour recalled, "It required a purpose-built two-storey building to house it."[8] This exercise proved that manual control of a guided weapon against an evading aircraft target was possible. Shorts was given the task of producing twelve missiles for flight tests against a real target.

Castlereagh thereby stood on the threshold of a rarefied new world. The function of anti-aircraft guided weapons is to intercept enemy aircraft and destroy or divert them before they can attack. To do this, the weapon has to identify the target, fire the missile, guide it to the target and detonate the warhead. Accordingly the weapon requires an engine to propel it, a guidance system and an explosive to destroy the target. At the launching point, on the ground or on board ship, the back-up technology must be able to find the attacking aircraft soon enough for the countermeasures to be taken, provide a launch platform, and a manned guidance system which can deliver the missile either to a direct hit or to detonate close enough to damage or destroy the attacking aircraft. Martin Armour has recalled a key moment as Shorts stood on the brink of the new world now opening before it:

I was sitting in my small office one day in the research department, bored to tears with the lack of anything to do. Into the office came Big Hugh. . and he planted himself on the edge of my desk as I had no room for a chair for visitors. . He said to me: "Armour, I'll give you some jobs to do. If I tell you how to do them, they'll be my responsibility. If I don't, they'll be yours." I don't ever remember him telling me how to do a job that he set me.

He told me of his plans to design a short-range ship-to-air defence weapon using as its basis the test vehicle we were producing in co-operation with RAE. He told me that if we were to achieve this we should have to bring in top engineers, experienced in missile design and others experienced in the installation of guns and radar and other equipment on ships. "In the meantime," he said, "we have to successfully complete our research contract with RAE and produce a test vehicle, however crude, which will satisfy them and the Navy that our aimer can guide a missile to destroy an aircraft that is attacking a ship. I want you to take on that job."

I don't know why he chose me, but I like to think he had made some inquiries about my background. When he recruited the key men to design the weapon and its ship equipment he made no mistakes. Money wasn't mentioned; however I found next month that my salary had gone up by about ten percent.[9]

Armour was soon to acquire important new colleagues at Castlereagh; and the enlarged team began to get into its stride.

NOTES

1   Conway was to be appointed to the board of Shorts in February 1955

2   Donne, op.cit., p127

3   Curt Johnson: Artillery – the Great Debate, in Weapons and Warfare of the 20th Century (London, 1975) p191

4   Martin Armour: I Remember (Belfast, 2002) pp 115, 119

5   George Jackson, interview with the author

6   Jackson, do. Armour, op.cit., p119

7   Jackson, unpublished memoir

8   Armour, op.cit., p 117

9   Armour, op.cit., pp117-8

5

TO THE ROCKET RANGE

FORTY *GPV's* were to be built. Almost all were fired, the first in 1953. One of the last to be made is preserved in the Science Museum, South Kensington, an indication of its title to a place in the history of post-war British engineering.

In reality much of the impetus came from the Germans. As the allied bombing campaign had mounted in 1943 and the option of invading England had become remote, Hitler devoted a disproportionate amount of scarce resources to pilotless bomb and rocket development. In the unreasoning optimism of the tyrant, he trusted that the V1 flying bomb and V2 rocket would still win him the war. The wartime reputation of German expertise was such that R.V. Jones, head of the scientific section of the Secret Intelligence Service in Whitehall, was confident that the V1 flying bomb of 1944 would prove to be rocket-powered. In fact it was not, although its Schmidt-Argus engine was, in several respects, even more ingenious.[1]

The V2 was a different matter: found to be 38 feet long and nearly six feet in diameter when RAF reconnaissance photographs were analysed, it took off almost vertically and, guided by gyroscopes, propelled itself to a height of 40 miles, with a velocity at the apex of about 2,250 mph. But Dr. Jones' was a lone voice in insisting to Churchill that the weapon on the launcher at Peenemunde was in fact a rocket. Lord Cherwell, the Prime Minister's most intimate scientific adviser, dismissed the possibility that German technology had reached such a point and maintained the objects were dummies planted to mislead. Jones, of course, was right: the V2 propelled a warhead of one to two tons into the stratosphere whence, alarmingly, more than 1,100 were to fall on London in the last months of the war.[2]

This was a formidable achievement of a revolutionary dimension; even if each rocket consumed some eight tons of scarce liquid oxygen and alcohol fuel in the process. More flying bombs would have accomplished the same offensive purpose much more economically, had not Hitler been so mesmerised by the potential of the rocket.

But there was still a jostling scramble among the Allies after the war to recruit the German scientists responsible for it. Its moving

Test Firing of the GPV supersonic Missile

spirit, Werner von Braun, narrowly escaped from the flames of the RAF raid on Peenemunde in August 1943, after rescuing some of his papers. He survived to master-mind the rocket development in the United States which was the foundation of the American post-war space programme. A colleague on the V2 team at Peenemunde, Willi Kretchmeyer, was recruited by the Rocket Propulsion Establishment at Westcott. The motors the Castlereagh team used for the *GPV* were in fact based on a design by von Braun's team, Kretchmeyer and their wartime colleagues who worked on the V2.

RPE were later to provide the rocket propulsion systems for succeeding generations of Shorts' missiles, up to and including *Starstreak*. Back in 1945 British and American expertise in rocket technology was broadly on a par. The divergence was to occur when the American effort began to respond to the investment of vast resources the United Kingdom could not match.

The *GPV's* guidance system relied on a ground-based radar which "illuminated" the target with pulses of energy. The guidance head was mounted in the nose, protected by a radar-transparent radome. It latched on to the pulses reflected from the target to determine its position and motion.

Propulsion was carried out in two stages. In the first, booster motors launched the missile and brought it up to flight speed. The eight rocket motors used solid propellant and were arranged in four pairs in a wrap-around arrangement. They accelerated the missile to Mach 1.2 - 912 mph – in the very short space of one and a half seconds. As the booster motors burned out, they were jettisoned from the missile by the action of explosive bolts.

The second stage consisted of a liquid-powered rocket motor which sustained the missile's speed for the remainder of its useful flight, lasting about 20 seconds. The volatile propellants, kerosene and oxygen-rich hydrogen test peroxide (HTP), were carried in seven tubular tanks positioned about the missile's centre of gravity. High-pressure nitrogen was used to expel the kerosene and HTP in such a manner as to maintain the missile's centre of gravity throughout the flight. The motor was fired 15 seconds before launch to ensure ignition occurred. During this interval the missile was held on the launcher by a pin which sheared when power was boosted. To meet safety requirements, an explosive charge was wrapped round the mid-section which could be detonated from the ground, breaking the missile into two unstable parts, should it diverge from its desired flight path.

The first stage booster motors were of an existing design, the Demon, using TNT high explosive as the propellant. The liquid-fuelled sustainer-motor for stage two and the fuel expulsion system were developed at RPE, which had facilities for the static firing of rocket motors.

After manufacture at Castlereagh, the *GPVs* were taken to Rochester in Kent where electronic engineers at Elliott Brothers fitted the guidance head. The trials were carried out at the Royal Aircraft Establishment's missile firing range at Aberporth on the south coast of Cardigan Bay. All the necessary facilities were available: tracking radars, receivers to marshal the data sent back by radio from the missile in flight, fixed and tracking film cameras and kine-theodolites which, in combination, monitored the launch, trajectory and entire flight behaviour.

George Jackson has recorded the nature of the complex procedure for a test firing at Aberporth. All of the systems, free of fuel and explosives, were first tested. Then the device was taken to a specially-adapted building where precise measurements were made, including weight and centre of gravity. From there it was moved to the explosives area. The emergency break-up charge and the booster rockets were fitted and the whole assembly placed on the loading trolley.

> The missile was now ready to be moved to the launching area when a firing slot had been agreed with the range authorities and the weather conditions were suitable. Once loaded on the launcher, the guidance, control and instrumentation systems were tested from a remote monitoring room behind a blast wall about 200 metres to the rear. When all systems were satisfactory, the launch area was cleared of all unnecessary personnel in preparation for fuelling. HTP is a very corrosive liquid, so during fuelling the required persons were dressed in protective clothing, including face masks. Fuelling took about an hour.
>
> The next stage was safety checks of all explosives circuits prior to arming and connecting the firing lines. All personnel were then cleared from the launch area and the missile was ready to enter a 30 – minute firing sequence.[3]

This involved further last-minute checking, with a verbal countdown every five seconds. At minus 15 seconds power was switched to the missile's own supply and the fixed cameras on the launcher were started. At minus 14 seconds the liquid-fuel rocket motor, which would take over from the booster launch rockets, was started, the missile being held on the launcher by the shear pin. At minus 10 seconds the verbal countdown increased to every second. At minus five the tracking and kine-theodolite cameras were started and at zero the booster rockets were fired.

One signal feature separated this procedure from reality: it could take up to four hours. There was also the unsolved problem of the extreme volatility of the HTP fuel, which caused the last three *GPVs* fired to blow up. Clearly, turning the *GPV* into the basis for a weapon system was going to involve elaborate innovation and development. Lesser spirits than the leadership at Castlereagh might have been discouraged by the chasm separating them from success. In Armour's words,

A tour of the factory floor and its conglomeration of worn-out machine tools, some of German and Italian descent left over from the war, reduced Conway to despair, but it also convinced him that, if ever we were to go into production with a weapon, we had to set up a whole new factory – which of course is exactly what he did.[4]

In 1956 Castlereagh won a further research contract to study the control of a short-range anti-aircraft missile using the system known as command line-of-sight. In this the operator monitors the flight of the missile through high-power binoculars, while controlling its direction with a joystick on top of which is fitted a thumb button. It is largely a Shorts creation and it is still the basis for the sophisticated short-range missiles Thales Air Defence produces from Castlereagh today.

The experts at the Royal Aircraft Establishment at Farnborough were satisfied that in this lay the answer to the question of developing a control system for a close-range weapon. Accordingly, Castlereagh began work on what became known as the *Green Light Test Vehicle*.

As Martin Armour has recorded, the RAE's idea of using various bits and pieces from obsolete test vehicles to fashion a new one proved to be practicable.[5] But certain of the components being in less

The Green Light Test Vehicle (GLTV) being exhibited at the Farnborough Air Show in 1957. Cdr Keith Burnett (left) and George Jackson (centre) discuss the motor for the GPV with a visitor

Preparation of the GLTV missile
for Flight Testing

than pristine state, it was to take the team two years of hard slog, involving much frustration, before they had a prototype ready for launching.

The first ballistic tests, to indicate in-flight behaviour of the *GLTV* but not involving control from the ground, were carried out at Larkhill, the Army's firing range on Salisbury Plain. Shorts' people found the RAE staff there most co-operative. The Army, based in Larkhill Barracks nearby, were less predictable. More than once a test vehicle was on the launcher ready for firing when the Royal Artillery began to dump shells into the guided weapons area. The low point was reached on the occasion when, with little warning, firing was abandoned for the day. It transpired that the Larkhill hunt was to enjoy the freedom of the range.

Meanwhile back in Castlereagh, the members of the research team were busy. Using their simulator experience, they predicted how the

GLTV would respond to the pre-programmed movements of its control surfaces. Later their prediction was compared to the actual behaviour in flight, as fed back to the ground. They were virtually identical. Armour was very impressed. But the computer programmer, Ruth Ball, a Queen's University graduate in both engineering and mathematics, looked at him rather disdainfully. "If your people will give us the right aerodynamic information," she said, "we will give you the right performance predictions." Told of this exchange later, a computer colleague observed that the whole thing was like a jumper. "You only get out of it what you put into it." From which Armour concluded that misfortunes blamed on computers should perhaps be taken with a grain of salt. But the accuracy of the research team's prediction was a good augury for the future; for the same expert men and women were to play a key part in the design and development of the *Seacat* ship-to-air guided missile.

But, despite this, as soon as the *GLTV* trials started in 1956, there was trouble over the hardware. Armour had already had difficulties with the components of the test vehicle the team had on the floor at Castlereagh. These were repeated on the launch pad at Aberporth, where the delays were beginning to cause anxiety. Christmas came and went and still there was no trial, although Shorts' contract with the Ministry of Supply was due to expire at the end of March. Conway ordered Armour to get over to Aberporth. He left the Great Northern Railway station in Great Victoria Street in Belfast on New Year's Eve via Dublin and Rosslare. The ferry reached Fishguard at 3 am and the customs men insisted on getting everyone up to check baggage. But it was nine o'clock before the Bedford van arrived to take the team through west Wales to their destination.

The trials team worked on a rota system which meant spending three weeks at Aberporth followed by three weeks at Castlereagh. Off-duty diversions in west Wales were limited. There was a cinema some miles from the guest house in which they lived and a golf course nearby. But it was the time of the Suez emergency and one of its domestic effects was the introduction of petrol rationing. In any case regulations ordained that the Bedford van was only to be used for "official" journeys. From time to time the definition of an official journey was to be rather vague.

The van was always filled on a Friday night when it left to convey the departing crew to the ferry at Fishguard. There were few pubs on the road, but the team soon ascertained those in which they would be made welcome. The Friday night call soon became a regular event.

The official driver was a reliable fellow who did not drink and drive; but the rest were free to put the cares of the week behind them – and had done so by the time the vehicle reached Fishguard. There a time-honoured ritual was observed, involving the departing personnel on the ferry lining the rail and loudly rendering the fishermen's hymn,

"For those in peril on the sea", for the alleged benefit of their colleagues left behind on the quay.

It was a bid by Martin Armour to circumvent the tedious journey via Rosslare and Fishguard which was to give him a further insight into Hugh Conway's persona. After one weekend at home, he resolved to try flying to London and taking the night train to west Wales.

> Who should I bump into on the plane but Big Hugh. "Where are you off to?" he asked, knowing full well I was supposed to be at Aberporth. "I've been home for a couple of days to see my family whom I haven't seen for a month," I told him. "How're you getting to Aberporth?" he asked. I explained to him that I had a berth booked on the midnight sleeper from Paddington to Carmarthen and that I would get a bus to Cardigan, where one of the boys would pick me up and take me to the base.
>
> As we were getting off the plane, he asked me to come back to his place. We got on a train and ended up at Marble Arch station. A short walk round the corner to Marble Arch Mews brought us to probably the most desirable residences in central London after Downing Street.
>
> Conway never did things by halves. The only person living in the flat at the time was his son, a student at London University. He was in shirt and pants, covered with dirt and oil and attempting to rebuild an ancient Austin Seven but had given up for the moment.
>
> 'What's the matter?' his father asked. 'It's that bloody fuel valve: I can't get it replaced.' 'It probably has a left-hand thread,' said his father. He had no interest in Austin Sevens. He was only interested in Bugattis and was the owner of one of the finest vintage models in the world, still capable of doing 80 miles an hour.
>
> But his father changed into overalls and slid under the Austin Seven. A few minutes later he handed out the faulty fuel valve, took the replacement from his son, came back out and said: "Try her now." At the first turn of the starting handle, the engine burst into life. Conway then suggested a cup of tea: he never drank alcohol. We had a cup and then I was on my way to Paddington.[6]

The cliff top test range at Aberporth, where runway lights had to be positioned, was wide open to the Irish Sea. The new arrivals were warned by the veterans from the *GPV* team, already on site, to keep on their pyjamas and to put everything else they had on top. It proved to be good advice, for the launcher of the test vehicle had to be set up in driving wind, sleet and snow. It was a frustrating six months, largely because of the condition of many of the components salvaged from old test vehicles, which the team was obliged to use for the new.

When the Castlereagh team arrived, the big aerospace companies were already well established at Aberporth and were paying large sums for use of the facilities. By contrast Shorts' activities were small beer and the team felt their many technical difficulties could have been regarded more sympathetically by the Aberporth management.

But from time to time native ingenuity was adapted to render life more tolerable. One example was the internal intercom on the site which comprised five rings, each company with a trials team being allocated its own. As Martin Armour explains:

> We had ring five and this allowed us to talk to any of our sites at Aberporth from the preparation room. However, when we were scheduled to carry out a trial we had to switch to ring one, which put us in touch with all the RAE sites. While on this ring we were not allowed to pass any messages to our own sites unless these were essential to the progress of the trial. On most occasions several hours passed before the trial could commence. During this time we were not able to contact our members at the launcher or at other sites to tell them that the tea was ready, a most important event.

> However during this waiting period there was considerable conversation on ring one in Welsh. We were suspicious that these conversations had little or nothing to do with the forthcoming trial. John, an Irish speaker in our team, suggested that we should get in on the act and he taught us to say, in Irish "Attention all Shorts' sites: the tea is ready". So on the next occasion that we were on stand-by on ring one, the message went out from the preparation room: . 'Ta an tae reidh.'

> Within minutes there was a call from the control room saying that we had transmitted a message which was not understood. I said that it had been a message passed between two of our members who were Irish speakers. There was a long period of silence and then the top man came on the phone. After hearing my explanation, he said that in future all communications on ring one should be conducted in English and I said I would instruct my staff to that effect. . We had no more conversations in Welsh on ring one.[7]

The testing of a missile is not easy. An aircraft can be flight tested from the manufacturer's own airfield, with information being fed back by the pilot or recorded by instruments installed on board. The exercise can be repeated indefinitely, unless the aircraft crashes. A missile, by contrast, requires a specially instrumented firing range where these unmanned airborne vehicles can be test-fired and the data gathered, all without endangering life and limb. Missiles are a one-shot device and for close-range weapons, like those developed by Shorts, the flight time is measured in seconds. For the research and design team, therefore, the vital data on performance, including control, guidance and flight characteristics, have to be gathered by radio link – by telemetry. This is supported by fixed and tracking cameras and radars.

Armour describes his six months at Aberporth in quest of a successful trial of the *GLTV*, frankly, as a purgatory. Only the unfailing cheerfulness of the members of his team, he admits, kept him sane. Shorts' research contract was due to end in March and pressure was mounting from Belfast to produce results. But week succeeded week as one problem was dealt with, only to be replaced by another. The weather was appalling during the first few months. There was uncertainty about the availability of the essential target aircraft from the RAF. But the unreliability of the cannibalised components provided by the RAE was by far the worst.

Armour, though, had kept Belfast fully informed by means of daily reports: prudence which was to pay off. Conway was able to use these to justify to the RAE an extension of the contract beyond March and this was duly granted. During April and May, in improved weather, the team fired eleven of its twelve test vehicles. After the eleventh the RAE called a halt, declaring that Shorts had made its point and they were satisfied. So the explosives were removed from the twelfth *GLTV* and the team packed up for the return to Belfast. The last test vehicle was on display at Castlereagh for many years.[8]

Despite the ups and downs at Aberporth, with its many frustrations, the experience the Shorts team gained there was vital to the new future opening before Castlereagh. As George Jackson recorded later, the Precision Engineering Division had proven the concept of a manually-controlled guidance system for a short-range missile; or, as Armour put it, they had demonstrated that a missile

Test Firing of one of the GLTV Missiles

could be guided visually by an aimer with sufficient accuracy to destroy an aircraft at short range. The importance of this success for Castlereagh, and indeed for the company as a whole, at that particular juncture can scarcely be over-estimated. The experience gained designing, building, testing and flight testing the *GPV* and the *GLTV* gave Castlereagh the expertise to progress in the guided weapons field.

Aberporth itself had been established by the Army in the early stages of the Second World War, to develop the rocket-launched shells which played such a spectacular part in the D-Day naval gunnery assault on Normandy in 1944. Essentially they consisted of a tube of cordite with a shell fitted in front. For ranging, the crewman adjusted the elevation: but he had no control over the missile in the guidance sense. As the war ended, gunnery was approaching its limits of sophistication. With the decline of the capital ship and the new dominance of air power, the way forward beckoned; and it led towards the weapons of a new generation: the guided missile.

In this rarefied stratum, structure, aerodynamics, propulsion, guidance and control each had to be integrated with the utmost precision; and the end product, however refined, had to be robust enough to survive the rigours, in a relatively short life, of rough handling and transportation under combat conditions, and of storage in all climates. The Castlereagh team, though, was eager to face the challenge.

NOTES

1   R.V. Jones: *Most Secret War* (London, 1978) p 370

2   Jones, op.cit., pp 430 – 461

3   Jackson, op.cit.

4   Armour, op.cit., p119

5   Armour, op.cit., p 120r

6   Armour, op.cit., p125-6

7   Armour, op.cit., p 123-4

8   Armour, op.cit., p127

6

Seacat

A S the radioactive dust settled over the desolation of Hiroshima and Nagasaki in the summer of 1945, navies worldwide faced a worrying future. Even if the nuclear threat were to be neutralised by the East-West stalemate, the other lessons of the war could not be gainsaid. They showed that a radical evolution had taken place. Pearl Harbor had been assumed to be impregnable and too shallow for submarines. Its corkscrew entrance, laced with steel-mesh netting, gave on to waters only seven fathoms deep - about forty feet. But this was seaborne torpedo and anti-submarine thinking. On 7 December 1941, the Japanese did employ midget submarines; but the spearhead and mass assault was provided by carrier-borne aircraft which had taken off 4,000 miles from their land bases. Their success was total, eliminating twelve US warships, sinking five of the nine battleships, killing 2,400 of their crews and wounding 1,100 others. But a significant, and little-noticed, aspect of the disaster was that all three American aircraft carriers, the *Lexington*, *Enterprise* and *Saratoga*, were at sea and escaped the bombardment. In the new age of air power, this was to be more important to the strategic course of the war in the Pacific than the loss of the battleships proved to be.

Three days after Pearl Harbor, the *Prince of Wales* and *Repulse*, under attack by Japanese torpedo bombers off the east coast of Malaya, perished with the loss of 840 of their crews. Never again would a commander-in-chief send capital ships into battle and to their death, having been deprived of their allotted airborne protection, as Winston Churchill did with the ill-fated Force Z.[1]

Yet the capital ship, clearly, was still essential in a new role: to provide the floating base enabling the supremacy of air power to be brought to bear. By 1950 the aircraft carrier had been accepted universally as the new core of the naval arm. It was the undisputed successor to the capital ship in its outmoded function of gun platform; and the massive ironclads, which represented the ultimate expression of that concept, were laid up, one by one, in dockyards and anchorages, waiting rooms for the scrapyard, never to fight again.

Opposite: The Electronic Pack Actuator Assembly (EPAA) in the clean air area of the Guided Weapons Production Unit (GWPU) at Queens Island

But the unsolved problem was how to protect the new fleet against bombs and airborne torpedoes. Patently, traditional gunnery would not be enough. The main anti-aircraft defence of the *Repulse*, a First World War battle cruiser, in its death throes off Malaya, had been eight elderly four-inch guns, hand-operated by deck crews in exposed and unprotected positions. But the *Prince of Wales*, less than nine months in service, had four twin 5.25in. turrets mounted on each side of the main deck, each gun capable of firing 18 rounds a minute at either ships or aircraft. For anti-aircraft fire she also carried six sets of eight-barrelled pom-poms, a 40mm. Bofors gun, plus light cannon and machine guns. The lesson for the Navy was clear: even the most modern battleship, fitted with the latest anti-aircraft gunnery systems, could be sunk by aircraft at sea.[2]

Accordingly, when Shorts measured up to the challenge of selling its *Seacat* concept to the Royal Navy, the logic of the most recent wartime experience was on its side. But if Admiralty minds had been concentrated and the strategic case made by the events of barely a decade before, there were tactical difficulties remaining.

One was finance. The Treasury climate was still austere. Justifying to the Ministry of Supply quantity production of an unknown new product, untested in battle, was difficult. The outbreak in 1950 of the Korean War, between Chinese-backed communist forces in the north and a United Nations-backed international anti-communist coalition in the south, did lead to an increase in armament budgets. But the Korean War was not a maritime struggle. Although five million died, it was not fought on an expansive scale: its prevailing character over the three years was exemplified in bitter and inconclusive slogging for a margin of earth, involving long-range artillery barrages and front-line skirmishes in which infantry hurled grenades from foxholes, while above the battlefield air mastery was contested by the new jet fighters. Viewed from Europe, therefore, where aviation had just scored a signal success barely a year before in defeating the Soviet attempt to blockade the American, British and French zones of occupied Berlin, it was not surprising that the new resources voted for rearmament were concentrated on military aircraft. So, on balance, the fact of rearmament in face of the communist threat did not make it materially easier for Shorts to plead its missile cause.

A persistent difficulty for the Belfast company was the old one of the existence of "the club": the circle of major mainland aviation manufacturers, each much larger and with immeasurably greater lobbying resources than Shorts could command, and from which, in its offshore base, it considered itself excluded. If a new project was on offer, the members of "the club" were accustomed to being given first pick of contracts. It was Hugh Conway's resolve that his company would not be excluded. The contract for *Green Light*, though, had stipulated that the object was to produce an experimental test vehicle and work was not to be influenced by any supposed weapons potential. Conway had no intention of doing all the spade-work required to prove that a manually - guided missile was the answer for the Royal Navy and then see a contract for a weapon handed out to a rival aircraft manufacturer, several of whom he knew to be waiting in the wings.[3]

Yet Shorts would be a late entrant. Guided weapons was a rarefied new field where the rival manufacturers, larger and more powerful, were already well established. They might resent a new competitor and, more important, might make this clear to the senior defence officials who had decisive influence on the placing of contracts and who were heavily dependent upon the resources of the big players.

In fact the new field embraced a vast and complex area which extended from short-range anti-tank projectiles to inter-continental missiles capable of delivering nuclear warheads over thousands of miles. Castlereagh's selected niche was the close-range anti-aircraft missile, with a range of up to six kilometres and designed for the defence of a ship, a land-based command post or other specialised military installation. Conway was convinced that the Navy would need such a weapon. But he also had the self-confidence, and the confidence in his technical team, to act upon his conviction, to the point of designing a prototype before there was any sign of a requirement for a weapon, still less a production contract, from the Ministry of Defence, the department inaugurated in 1946 to co-ordinate the work of the old Services ministries and which, in 1964, was to replace them. Typically Conway resolved to back his hunch and soldier on without either requirement or contract.

It was a brave departure, for to design an operational weapon was a much more ambitious challenge, both technical and financial, than producing an experimental test vehicle where the client was picking up the tab. *Green Light*, minus any proximity fuse or warhead, could sit on its launcher at Aberporth, its crew armed with four minutes warning of the approach of the target aircraft. If the weather was bad they would be unlikely to be there at all. In any case there was plenty of time to switch on the batteries and bring the oil supply up to pressure, only then removing the weatherproof cover. A weapon would have to sit on its launcher on the pitching deck of a warship, tossed in ocean squalls and awash with the swell, in Arctic cold and tropical heat. The crew would be called to action stations and the aimer would take up position. He would have five seconds, perhaps less, to line up the missile on the target spotted by the lookout. In that brief interval, electrics, hydraulics, fuse and propulsion would instantly have to be activated.[4]

Conway's approach was two-pronged. First, he recruited a new Assistant Chief Engineer, Guided Weapons, as well as some Admiralty engineers familiar with the harsh weapons environment on board ship.

John Dent, the new Assistant Chief Engineer, arrived at Castlereagh early in 1955, between the trials of GPV and the decision to press ahead with *Green Light*. Dent was a London graduate who had served his apprenticeship at the Rolls Royce aero engine plant at Derby. Five years before he came to Belfast he had attended the first guided weapons trials on the Woomera Range in South Australia. Since 1944 he had been principal scientific officer at the Admiralty Gunnery Establishments, first at Teddington and later at Portland in Dorset, working on servo systems with the guided weapons group. He had also experience of the RPE's project at Westcott, RTV1, and was later to work with Armstrong Whitworth, Hawker Siddeley and Pirelli. He subsequently became managing director of Dunlop and was knighted in 1986 on his retirement as chairman of the Civil Aviation Authority. He died in 2002. In Dent's five years at Shorts from 1955, George Jackson found him tremendously impressive as an inspirational leader.

> "A very good engineer .. hands-on guy. He wasn't sitting up in the office. He was down on the floor – wanting to know what was going on. So things started to move forward".[5]

Armed with the considerable expertise of the existing team, Conway gave the go-ahead for work to start drawing up an in-house specification for the close-range, line of sight missile he had in mind. As Martin Armour has recorded, the team already had been busy scouring all potential sources of intelligence, including the aviation press, civil servants in Defence and contacts in the Navy, to ascertain the parameters of official thinking. With these in mind, they fixed upon a chosen range and armament and John Dent produced outline plans of several possibilities. One day in 1956 Conway came into the office Armour and his colleague shared, interrogated Armour and his colleague closely; then he drew a line round one of the configurations. "Get started," he said.

Seacat was under way. But the technical challenge was formidable, as Armour with notable lucidity has explained:

> The problems for which there had been no previous solutions were the gyroscope, which was necessary to stabilise the weapon in flight, and the batteries, which were needed to provide power for the guidance and control systems and for the fuse. The missile also required hydraulic oil pressure to operate its control surfaces. There was no way we could envisage a weapon sitting on a launcher for long periods with its gyroscope running and its batteries fully charged and its hydraulic system pressurised. What we needed was a gyroscope at rest, an inert battery and an unpressurised oil system, all of which could be activated and brought into operation within a few seconds of the firing button being pressed. None of our contacts at the RAE or in the aircraft industry was able to help.[6]

But by a combination of ingenuity and good luck these problems were to be solved. One of the guided weapons team at Castlereagh proposed using the pressure provided by the rocket motor to power the hydraulic system. This idea was adopted and, in refined form, is still in use in the latest missiles.

A Scottish company, newly-established as the British subsidiary of an American parent, came to the rescue on the batteries. They made special batteries for the mining industry, but British interest in the product had been slight. One day, touting for further potential clients in the aviation industry, the Chief Executive telephoned Shorts and was put through to Armour. Without appreciating just why these Scottish- American batteries were so special and bearing in mind that Castlereagh had already exhausted all its contacts in the domestic battery industry without result, he asked this man to call.

He proved to be an unassuming engineer rather than a high-powered salesman and Armour admitted afterwards that his visitor had not got very far in his description of his special battery when his colleague and he felt like locking the door in case he got away. For what he was offering were storage cells safe for use in coal mines where combustible gas is a recurrent danger. Accordingly the batteries were inert: i.e., they were unable to convey current – until a charge of thermite (the same powdered aluminium and iron oxide as is used in incendiary bombs and in welding) fitted within them was ignited. Thermite produces a very high temperature and the resultant heat brought the batteries up to full voltage in a fraction of a second. There were still technical problems to be sorted out; but the team, vitally, had found its battery.

The search for the right kind of gyroscope meant going abroad. A gyroscope, fundamentally, is a simple thing. It consists of a small flywheel with a heavy rim. The wheel is mounted on an axle in a circular frame so that it can rotate at high speed in any direction. It was a common upmarket toy in the 1930s, when youngsters would spin the flywheel by pulling a rip cord wound round the axle and then balance the gyroscope on a piece of string held taut. Its key characteristic is that, once in motion, it resists any change in the direction in which it is rotating. This makes it ideal for ships' stabilisers, the autopilots of airliners - and for guided weapons.

The team at Castlereagh tackled the search for the right kind of gyroscope by a process of elimination. The Cold War was at its most frigid. The team did not know what was going on within the Soviet Union. But they knew that the Americans, the Australians and the French were involved in guided weapons. The British were preoccupied with long-range missiles. Short-range weapons were being developed in Australia and France; but they were anti-tank, designed to hit a slow-moving target, not anti-aircraft. The team learned, however, that the French were using a quick-start gyroscope.

Hugh Conway decided to pay them a visit. He found that the French company wanted a prohibitive sum to licence the gyroscope to Shorts. But all was not lost. The French conceded that he could not consider terms without being given sight of the product; and, having seen it, he quickly grasped the principle upon which it operated. It proved to be a sophisticated version of the turbine developed originally by the Greek mathematician, Hero of Alexandria, in AD 100, consisting of a hollow ball with two spouts on opposite sides. The ball was mounted on bearings allowing it to rotate. When partially filled with water and heated to boiling point, the steam emerging from the spouts caused the ball to rotate. The French had replaced the steam with explosive which, when ignited, caused the ball, fitted in a framework, to rotate at high speed and form the "wheel" of the gyroscope.

Conway decided that the French could not claim patent rights on a principle nearly 2,000 years old. So the Castlereagh team, enlisting the aid of an explosives company, again in Scotland, developed a gyroscope capable of attaining a speed of 40,000 revolutions a minute within a fraction of a second.

The instant-start, cordite driven, gyroscope developed for the *Seacat* weapon system

Conway then invited EMI, the Electrical and Musical Industries combine, to design a proximity fuse. The Government's ordnance research department designed a continuous rod warhead to fit within the dimensions of the missile body. This consisted of looped metal rods which, when exploded, could cut an aircraft in half.

Castlereagh was now ready to submit its proposal for missile, shipboard launcher and director to the Government, presenting it as the answer to the new menace of the fast, low-flying aircraft, low enough to evade defensive radar. As yet there were no sea-skimming offensive missiles; but there were torpedoes. Widespread consultation took place while the Shorts team waited. Then an official specification was issued for a manually-guided close-range missile for the defence of the fleet.

"If Shorts had written it themselves," said Armour, "it could not have been more in line with our proposed design" The omens indeed were good. A high-powered team of civil servants from procurement and research plus officials from the Admiralty visited Castlereagh to assess the proposal on the ground and to gauge the extent of production facilities. Conway led the Shorts team, giving a masterly presentation of their missile's potential; and the Shorts effort was backed up by their sub-contractors, led by EMI, who provided an impressive earnest of their commitment by arriving in Belfast with a complete fuse assembly in their baggage.

As for manufacturing facilities, there was no room at Castlereagh for quantity production of a missile; but Conway had earmarked space at the main Queen's Island site, suitably remote from aircraft assembly. Upon this he proceeded to impose a modicum of spit and polish, both as a means of dramatising for all involved the importance to the company of the new departure, and of extending to it the sort of discipline he knew would impress a military customer.

"You Irish are an untidy lot," he said to Martin Armour in a typical provocative throwaway remark. "So I'm going to make sure you don't foul up this lot!" Accordingly, the missile plant-to-be was washed down and redecorated. The air conditioning was adjusted so that air pressure was higher inside than out. Windows were sealed and air locks fitted to the entrance doors; so there was no inflow of unfiltered air. White overalls, hats and sandals were provided and made compulsory wear for all personnel in the facility.

Conway's momentum as a manager was derived in large measure from an innate optimism: he was a positive thinker. In the case of *Seacat*, he knew the Navy needed a close-range weapon and he was confident that Shorts' proposed design was good enough to be precisely what the Navy needed: i.e., a replacement for the old Bofors gun, but with greater range and striking power. In addition it had to be relatively simple, cheap and capable of being fitted to existing

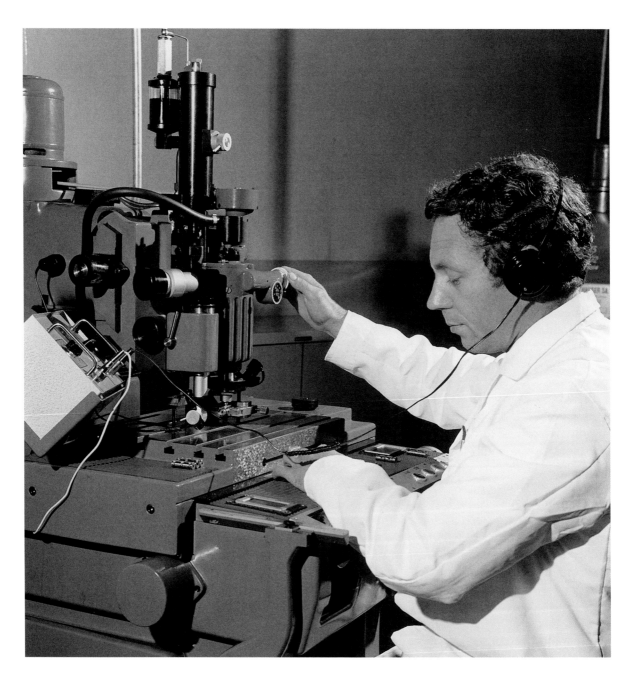

Jig grinding the hydraulic spool valves for the *Seacat* missile. The holes were ground to a tolerance of 0.00005in or – in modern parlance – to a tolerance of 1.2micron, by listening for the correct tone from the grinder.

warships as uprated equipment; unlike *Seaslug,* the long-range anti-aircraft missile of the 1950s, where the ship providing the platform was actually designed round the missile.[7] He was proven to have been right in 1957, when the first *Seacat* production contract for the Royal Navy was placed with Shorts. But, as George Jackson later put it, "that was when the problems started –

Because of the nature of the thing and the tight time scale involved, it wasn't possible for us to build a complete missile. We didn't have anywhere we could put explosives into it. One of the peculiarities of *Seacat* was that it was made up of a kit of parts. EMI made the fuse. We

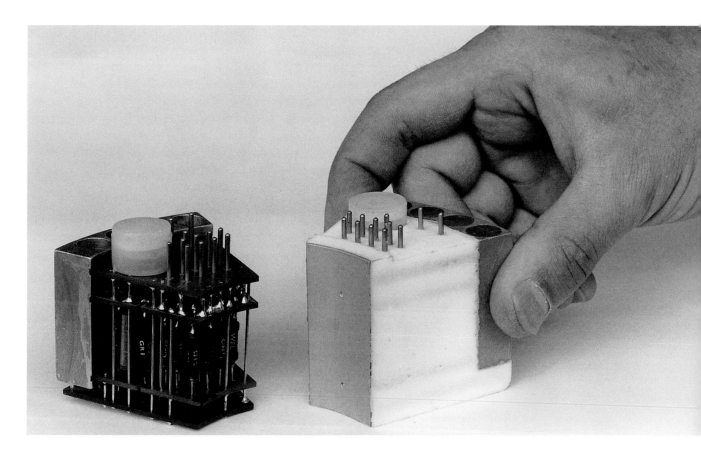

Part of the thermionic valve
pack before and after potting
to ensure robustness

didn't have the expertise, so we subcontracted to EMI. The warhead had to be made on one of the armament depots, so that was subcontracted. We built the electronics. We built the airframe. We did all the control systems, the guidance system and the wings. The motor we couldn't do anything with because they again required particular expertise. You have to machine cordite to fit into the motor casing. We hadn't the backup or facilities to work with explosives.

During development the sub-assemblies were manufactured in various parts of the UK then assembled into a complete missile at Aberporth. Later, when *Seacat* was in service, assembly was done at the Royal Naval Armament Depots. At Castlereagh we never actually saw a missile put together, apart from a mock-up. The Navy had all these armament depots where they did all their assembly of shells. They were used to handling explosives. So all we had to do was to train them to assemble a missile.[8]

This involved bringing Royal Navy armaments personnel from the various depots to Castlereagh for training. *Seacat* was now in mass production, so the naval engineers had to be taught how to test the product once assembled. This demanded a range of test equipment which, in turn, had to be provided by Castlereagh. But the Navy were doing the final assembly in their depots, testing the missiles, packing them in their containers and then delivering them on board ship. In fact having the client doing this worked very well.

But the missile on its own was only part of the story. It also had to be launched, and – once launched – guided. For in itself it was merely a very sophisticated round of ammunition, stored against the day of use in a magazine on board ship, ready for firing without any pre-launch checks. To quote Jackson again: "There wasn't a missile in service anywhere in the world at that time which had achieved this."

To do it, the missile required ship equipment involving a launcher, a computerised control console and a director.

NOTES

1   The new aircraft carrier, Indomitable, completed only ten weeks before at Vickers Armstrong, Barrow, had been earmarked for the vital escort duty, but ran aground while working-up in the West Indies and was under repair.   It was the Prime Minister's personal decision that the two battleships would go ahead without air cover of their own. [Winston S. Churchill: *The Second World War, vol. III* (London, 1950) p524; Richard Hough: *The Hunting of Force Z* (London, 1974) p238].

2   Arthur Hezlet: *Aircraft and Sea Power* (London, 1970) p208

3   Armour, op.cit., p128

4   Armour, op.cit. p129

5   Jackson, interview with author

6   Armour, op.cit., p129

7   Jackson, interview with author

8   Do

The Navy Approves

AS the pace of development gathered speed, Castlereagh steadily grew in size. The core team of 15 which had existed in the early days in 1951 was to expand to more than 250 by the time *Seacat* was accepted into service by the Royal Navy in 1962. But at the beginning the team knew little about the missile business. Work on the *GPV*, however, though it had no commercial future, introduced them to it. It was a process of exploration. The young engineers who came to Castlereagh from Queen's Island in January 1952 were strictly aircraft types, but on that count used to working with the lightweight metal alloys which form the core of that industry and which are such a vital element in guided weapons. Most of them, still in their 20s and 30s and eager to learn, had heard that the company was diversifying and that there were going to be opportunities to work on missiles. They seized the chance to get in on the ground floor.

George Jackson had been in the RAF working on ground radar during the Second World War. On demobilisation he came over to Northern Ireland with the Ministry of Civil Aviation as a member of the communications staff at Nutt's Corner in County Antrim. This had been a wartime RAF base and was then being converted for use as an embryonic civil airport to serve the city of Belfast. Jackson was soon involved in preparations for the installation of ground control approach radar. He moved to Shorts at the end of 1952.

Over the five-year period culminating in *Seacat's* acceptance trials, new and close relations were fostered with the sub-contractors providing fuse, warhead, batteries, flares and many lesser components, thereby locking Shorts back into the mainland industry in a manner the company knew would be vital to its survival.[1] Shorts had keen support from these partners. The post-war aviation industry was in a volatile state and all were hungry for work. But nothing was yet in the bag. In replacing the Bofors gun of 1936, which was the standard medium anti-aircraft gun in the Second World War for the British, American and Russian forces, the Seacat would fill the gap left by a venerable weapon firing 40mm shells but with a ceiling of 16,250 feet- or more than three miles. *Seacat* commanded a range of three and

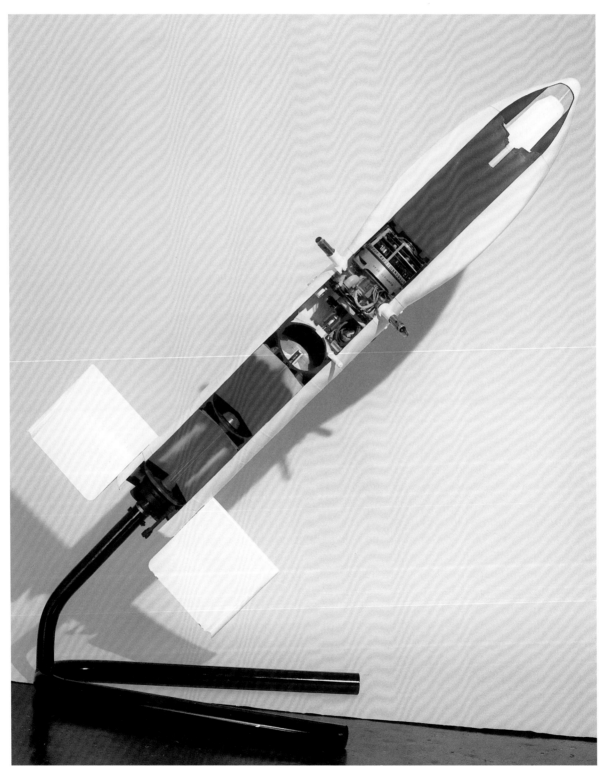

The *Seacat* missile sectioned to show the key elements including the EPAA and aft of it, the oil reservoir.

three quarter miles or about six kilometres, its round basically being a cylinder with a modest length of less than five feet. In fact it measured four feet eleven inches by seven and a half inches diameter and weighed only 140 pounds but with a warhead weighing 45 pounds. There were four swept-back wings to provide control surfaces at the centre and four stabilising fins at the rear. Except for the welded steel motor casing, all sections were made of aluminium alloy.

It was a tactical missile, eschewing the gunnery doctrine of a curtain of fire in favour of guiding specific rounds to a selected target. Shorts was to claim that it would provide an effective close-range defensive screen for naval vessels whose air arm and longer-range guided weapons had been by-passed or defeated. As George Jackson summarised the thinking,

> The aircraft of the vast majority of countries at that time relied upon conventional bombs, torpedoes, air-to-surface unguided rockets and gunfire as anti-ship weapons. Therefore weapon release occurred at less than two thousand yards from the target, well inside the effective 'kill' range of *Seacat*. The subsonic operational speed of *Seacat* gave the missile a very short range capability, contributing to its efficiency in surprise and multiple attacks, or in battle where radar is unable to cope with the number of hostile aircraft.

The *Seacat* Director for the basic Mark 20 system

Simplicity was the essence of the approach, the operating system being entirely visual, with the aimer tracking the target through binoculars and guiding the missile, in its flight of thirty seconds or so, to intercept it.

> The guidance signals were generated by movement of a thumb-operated joystick and transmitted to the missile via radio link. The guidance system measured the position of the missile relative to the target and adjusted its flight path to bring about interception. The command link guidance system is the least complex. Most of the guidance components are located at the launch site. The missile carries the bare minimum of equipment, increasing its reliability and minimising the cost of each shot.[3]

In practice it was found possible to fit *Seacat* into British and foreign fire control systems with great success. Complete fire control from below decks was achieved. Using both radar and television cameras,

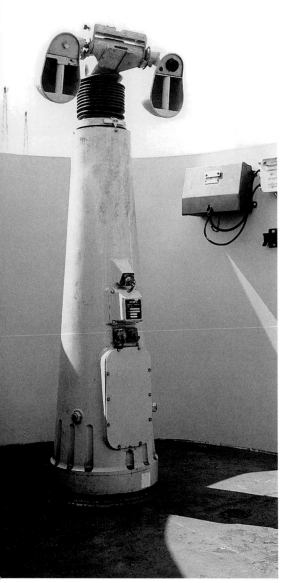

The Pedestal Director used as a
fallback for the automatic system. A
variant of this, the Target Designation
Sight, is still in use on board RN
vessels.

the *Seacat's* deviation from the sight-line was measured and
correction signals fed to the missile so that it coincided with the
target. The information about both missile and target meanwhile
was displayed on a below-decks screen. But the aimer could still
override the automatic system. In addition a director was
positioned on deck as fallback in an emergency.

The rocket motor itself was the work of Imperial Metal
Industries, using solid propellant with dual charges, the boost
charge to accelerate the missile to 750 feet per second (500
miles/hour), and the sustainer charge to maintain that velocity
throughout the remainder of its useful flight. The four tail fins
were bolted to the rear of the motor casing and set to 45 degrees
to the wings. They contained flare tubes along their tips to allow
the aimer to visually track the missile.

Shorts' missile, marking the formal entry of the company into
the new field of guided weapons, was shown to an interested
professional audience at the Royal Aircraft Establishment show at
Farnborough in 1959. It was a proud moment for the Castlereagh
team. But was it, in essence, so remarkable? Among those who
noted the event was a wartime pilot of RAF Bomber Command
who, at the age of 44, had since risen to become Managing
Director of Imperial Chemical Industries' Metals Division and was
later to be knighted, St. John Elstub. After leaving the RAF, Elstub,
who had gone from Rugby School to the University of Manchester
and was a qualified mechanical engineer, had been appointed
Superintendent of the Rocket Propulsion Department of the
Ministry of Supply. Two years later he rejoined ICI, with whom he
had been before the war. As he later explained,

> We took over a wartime ammunition factory at Summerfield, near
> Kidderminster, and I had a free hand, within reason, to pick up my
> own team from within ICI. We designed and built the first rocket
> motor, a large booster of 140,000 lb. total impulse. We designed and
> built the plant to make it; we built the static range; and we fired the
> first rocket successfully all within one year of signing the contract.

> The lesson that comes out of this to me very strongly is that, with
> a small, dedicated team of enthusiasts, and given a clearly defined
> objective, you can move mountains. The difficulty in other walks of
> life is to define the objectives equally clearly, and it is far harder to
> generate the same enthusiasm in a larger team. [4]

Summerfield went on to develop the two stage motor used on *Seacat*.
As George Jackson was to add: "Elstub's remarks about the
momentum generated by a small dedicated team surely applied to
Castlereagh in the early days."[5]

The *Seacat* quadruple launcher
armed and ready for action.

Development trials of *Seacat* began at Aberporth in 1959. Having been completed satisfactorily, two years later the vital matter of sea trials loomed. The Royal Navy nominated HMS *Decoy*, a Daring class destroyer, typical of the long-range craft planned towards the end of the Second World War with the Pacific theatre in mind. The class, consisting of eleven vessels of 2,800 tons displacement, represented a good example of how the swift development of guided weapons was affecting naval craft. The 4.5in. turrets were radar-controlled; but, as all-gun destroyers, by the 1950s they were effectively obsolete.

The *Decoy* was based at Plymouth, conveniently close to the Royal Naval arms depot at Saltash. While civilian workers ashore were assembling and testing fuses, warheads and guidance and control units in the depot and packing them in their weatherproof canisters, the *Decoy* was temporarily fitted with a quadruple *Seacat* launcher. Meanwhile the Castlereagh squad had designed a missile trainer which was later installed on board ships as a ship trainer. The concept of this was simple, as Martin Armour has explained –

The first *Seacat* firing off HMS *Decoy* in April 1962.

The trainer had a screen upon which were displayed two spots of light. One moved around the screen, representing an attacking aircraft. The other was under the control of the aimer's thumb. It was his job to try to keep the second spot on top of the first one. HMS *Decoy* sent us some of the 40mm gun crews and we gave them instruction. Eventually we selected three of them to be *Seacat* aimers.

The best of them was an ordinary seaman who had a poor reputation on the ship for lateness in returning from leave. But over the years he gained quite a reputation for himself as an expert aimer. But during the trials we found that the aimer, with his thumb-operated joystick was asking the missile to manoeuvre in ways in which aerodynamically it was incapable of doing....This was going to be a major setback but one of Hugh Conway's recruits came up with the answer. We did not have to touch the missile. He added a computer element to the ship's signal processing unit which calculated if the demand the aimer put in was within the capabilitites of the missile – and if not, reduced it. After all these years this system is still used in piloted aircraft which scream across the sky and do 9g turns – But the pilot cannot ask his aircraft to do the impossible.[6]

Seacat was never to be permanently installed on the *Decoy* or any of her ten sister destroyers. Like many craft laid down in a hurry in wartime and later developed in peacetime fits and starts during a period of rapid innovation, the *Daring* class earned an unwanted reputation for troublesome electrics. *Decoy* in due course was sold to Peru, renamed the *Ferre* and handed over by her new owners to Cammell Laird of Birkenhead for comprehensive refit, in the course of which eight surface-to-surface French *Exocet* tactical missiles were added. But this was a minor detail when set against the successful outcome of the *Seacat* trials. After further tests of the explosives warhead off Malta, the Admiralty expressed itself satisfied and duly acted upon its approval by placing the vital first production contract.

Seacat already commanded international attention. As an anti-aircraft missile in what was a sophisticated business, it was cheap. Estimates of the cost per round, depending upon how much of the back-up equipment was taken into account, varied between £5,000 and £10,000. In guided weapons, this was chickenfeed. As a result the new arrival was a matter of interest to a wide spectrum of middle-ranking states with coasts to defend and an interest in ship-borne anti-aircraft defence. In fact the first vessel to fire the production missile was not British at all, but Swedish. The Swedish Navy was fascinated by the *Seacat* concept from the start and a defence team had visited Belfast frequently. A former officer in the Swedish Navy, Commander Bob Nordenfelt, was appointed Shorts' resident engineer in Stockholm and a team from Shorts went out to lay on a demonstration in 1961. The Swedes watched this and found that the hardware was doing everything that had been promised in the data given to them from the British trials. Although they were never to

Seacat firing from the Swedish vessel Södermanland, one of four Ostergötland class fitted with *Seacat*.

conduct any trials of their own, they placed an order shortly afterwards and *Seacat* was installed on four of their *Ostergötland*-class frigates. Later Martin Armour was one of the party from Shorts invited to witness the first production firing of the missile.

I was somewhat apprehensive when I found they had a minute by minute programme laid down for the firing, with full press, radio and TV coverage. After several years' experience with delays, catastrophic failures and spectacular misses during the development testing of *Seacat* at Aberporth Guided Weapons Range and on board HMS *Decoy*, I was not entirely happy about the confidence of the Swedish Navy.

We and the press and various VIPs from the Swedish defence department boarded a high-speed launch at the naval base of Karlskrona on the south-east coast. It was an uneventful trip, until after about half an hour we found ourselves heading at full speed towards a cliff. Pulses quickened and hearts missed beats until suddenly there was a gap ahead and we went through this gap at full speed with only about half a beam's width to spare on either side - and there ahead of us was the Swedish destroyer armed with *Seacat.*

Seacat was designed for instant firing. There was no countdown; but for the benefit of the media they gave us a four minute countdown. Spot on 1500 hrs. *Seacat* climbed into the sky. Absolutely perfect.![7]

Murphy's Law having been seen off in such style, Armour then recorded that he could not really recall what happened afterwards, he was so overcome with pride in Shorts' achievement and admiration for the organisational talents of the Swedish Navy. Perhaps the entertainment provided by one of the naval officers at his home, where the party duly repaired to watch the day's events on the television news from Stockholm, might have had something to do with it!

At such an early stage in its weapon life, all this provided priceless exposure for *Seacat.* The Royal Navy was slow enough in the early stages to act upon its interest in the missile. Shorts was obliged to undertake one of the hardest of its hard sells. The company found itself up against one of the most difficult commercial adversaries - tradition. For centuries British ships had ruled the waves and that rule had been enforced by British guns. To be obliged to accept that a seemingly puny little missile was more potent than a gun, even an anti-aircraft gun, involved a leap of faith which a few of the more elderly sea dogs proved reluctant to make. But once the vital production contract was placed, everything changed. The Navy laid on every facility for the overseas agents who wanted to watch *Seacat* at work at close quarters. Inquiries from abroad began to come in immediately it became known that Great Britain had ordered the new weapon. It was possible for Shorts also to talk costs. *Seacat* was now airborne in the financial sense as well.

NOTES

1   Flares were emitted from the missile in flight to provide a clear visual check of its trajectory for the aimer.

2   Jackson, interview with the author

3   Jackson, op.cit.

4   Presidential address to the Institution of Mechanical Engineers, 1974, quoted by Jackson, op.cit

5   Jackson, op.cit

6   Armour, op.cit., p 134

7   Armour,op.cit; pp 136–7

8

WHITEHALL POLITICS

THREE years after he recruited John Dent to deepen the pool of experience in the young team at Castlereagh, Hugh Conway made a decision which was to prove important when he invited another young engineer to join the team. At 35, Philip Foreman had spent fifteen years in the Scientific Civil Service. He had come to Conway's notice because of his work on the design of the deck launcher for Seacat. Conway resolved that he must have Foreman inside the company and on the Castlereagh team.

Like many young men before and since, Philip Foreman had adopted his chosen career by travelling along a road whose course was influenced by many factors not all of which had to do with the job itself. He was born in 1923, in the Suffolk village of Exning, just outside Newmarket, where his father's family worked in the racing stables. He is not aware of any engineering tradition in his family. (His mother was the daughter of a police officer in Manchester.) But while he was still a child, his father took a job as a tractor driver on a Cambridgeshire farm. Although there was nothing to indicate it at the time, this was to have an important influence on his future.

He went to the local Church of England school and then, on a scholarship, to the grammar school in the neighbouring village of Soham. But, for ten years, he came home to live and breathe the constant activity which was the life of a busy East Anglian farm. Prominent in its daily course were the mechanics of farm equipment. His father had left school at twelve and had no mechanical training, but his aptitude was such that he had assumed control of installation, repair and maintenance of the entire stock of farm machinery.

As Philip Foreman was to recall, he was receiving a very valuable introduction to things mechanical, although he was not to realise the importance of it at the time. But he was aware that his mechanical interest had been aroused because he had the passion for *Meccano* construction and for model steam engines characteristic of so much of the youth of the 1930s.

When the Second World War broke out in September 1939, Foreman had just taken his school certificate and, at the age of sixteen, was determined to leave home and earn his living. But it often proves to be the case that the jobs a young person fails to get exercise as great an influence upon their future as those they do. In fact he was turned down for two unexciting clerical posts in local offices and, backed by wise parents, went back to school for two more years. It was at this stage that the vital spark of endeavour was to be lit. As he admitted later,

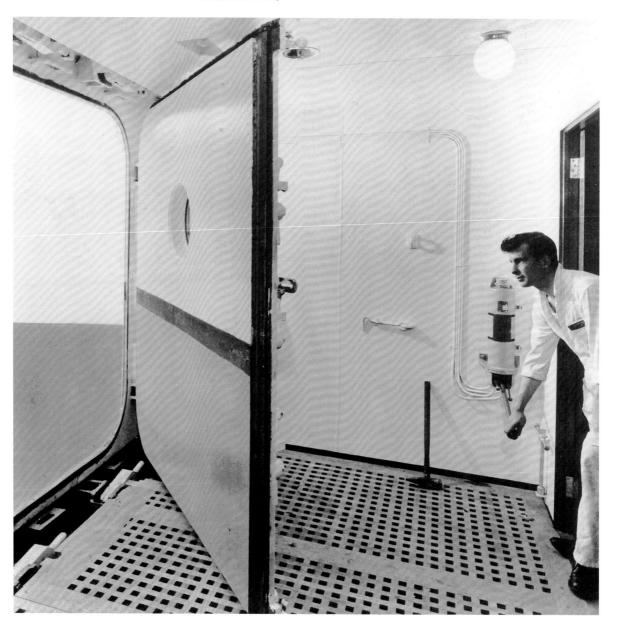

Hydraulic rams designed and built for the doors of P & O Liner, Canberra. One of a range of products designed during the mid – 1960s.

My time was spent more on sport than in academic advancement, until the woodwork master brought to my attention the existence of the British Empire Open Scholarships to Loughborough College. I decided to try for one – much to the disapproval of the headmaster, who told me that I had no chance and would only let the school down by entering! At school I had the reputation of being single minded so, characteristically, I went ahead, with tremendous support and encouragement from other masters, who gave me free extra-curricular tuition in their own time.

I went to Loughborough College to take the examination (the first time I had ever been away from home) and succeeded... But the scholarship only covered the cost of tuition and I had to borrow money from the local education authority to help me through two years of residence there.[1]

Foreman was to leave Loughborough in 1943, not only with a first in the Mechanical Engineering Diploma, but also with a good grounding in what industry and manufacture was about. In the difficult years ahead, the nature of this was to play a vital part in ensuring the survival of Shorts, and its trailblazing Castlereagh offshoot, on occasions when politicians, whose gaze did not range beyond the next general election, wished to close it down. He acknowledged his debt to Loughborough.

Research into solar power resulted in this parabolic mirror made from fibreglass with reflective *Melinex* glued to it

The *Diamo Hogger* was used to trim green logs direct from the forest for use in fencing. Smaller thinnings were trimmed in a *Diamo Chipper*. The resulting chips were then dispatched for the manufacture of chipboard.

The resulting posts and fencing installed along the motorway.

Although I know it is not today fashionable, I believe that week about in lectures and college workshops in a commercial environment (where we had to clock in and actually produce engineering products for sale) is an excellent way of educating and training professional engineers, for it gives them theory and practice side by side…It does produce good, honest, practical engineers who at least can relate academic work to the real world of engineering and commerce.[2]

In fact in future years Foreman was to feel obliged to let go talented designers in his company whose inspiration was seen to be failing the vital, if brutal, cost-effective test of what would sell in an international market.

But back in 1943 the war was well into its fourth year: the Wehrmacht had been thrown back by the Red Army before Stalingrad; after Alamein, Rommel was in headlong retreat in North Africa; even the battle against the U-boats in the north Atlantic, influenced by the breaking of the Nazis' Enigma codes, was turning in the allies' favour; and their heavy bombers were pounding German cities, day and night. Foreman, like most able-bodied youths, was keen to get involved. His grandfather had been in the Navy in the First World War, but when he volunteered he was dismayed to be rejected on account of colour blindness. Instead he was told to join the Royal Naval Scientific Service, a kind of half-way house where civil servants engaged upon naval work:

Argument was to no avail and the only choice I was given was between the Admiralty Research Laboratory at Teddington and the Naval Ordnance Department at Bath. I opted for Teddington as being nearer to home, which was important to me on a salary of only £200 per annum as a Temporary Experimental Assistant Grade 3 and the local education authority loan to repay…I was allocated to a department charged with the design and development of hydraulic servo-systems for both the Navy and the Army. [3]

This indeed was the shape of things to come; for the servo is an engineering device providing automatic powered control of a larger apparatus, as in the steering and brakes of the modern car. In wartime one of the most urgent applications was in the remote control of artillery, particularly anti-aircraft guns. Much of Foreman's early work was associated with the remote control of that very celebrated Bofors 40mm gun upon which nearly all armies relied heavily throughout the war and to which the brash young newcomer, *Seacat*, was eventually to prove itself the able successor. A later project was the design for the launcher for the missile itself. Conway duly asked Foreman whether he would come to Shorts to join the guided weapons team in Belfast, assuming responsibility for the design and development of all the shipborne and armament depot equipment associated with the *Seacat* project. It was a major decision for a young English engineer with a secure Admiralty job in the civil service; but, looking back in retirement from his home, high above the waters of Belfast Lough and the Shorts/Bombardier complex, he had no regrets; satisfied that he would not have achieved such a fulfilling career anywhere else.

The Galvanic Skin Resistance Meter measured the electrical resistance across the palm in order to assess response to disturbing stimuli – A Lie Detector

Having accepted Conway's invitation in 1958, the eventual trials installation of *Seacat* on HMS *Decoy* represented both Foreman's last project as an Admiralty employee (the deck launcher) and his first as an employee of Short Brothers (the visual director from which the complete system is controlled). Ahead, as he described it, lay one deep end after another. Within three years he had been appointed Chief Engineer of the Guided Weapons Division, three years after that, Company Chief Engineer and, in 1967, Managing Director, within nine years of joining the firm.

Coming from the civil service he was surprised to find, not fewer meetings and paperwork, but more. Where the

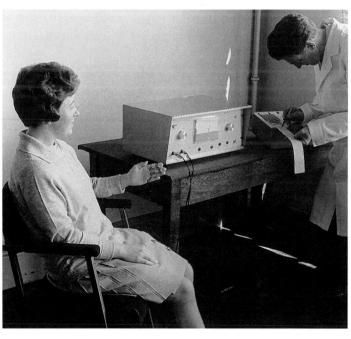

overriding concern in the service had been technical excellence, handed down by people of undoubted top scientific calibre, he found in industry a very feet-on-the-ground appreciation of the need to design for production – and a greater urgency to get things done. But to his satisfaction he found he had joined a guided weapons design team, at the time some 200 strong, which was closely-knit, dynamic, progressive in its thinking and highly-motivated. As he got to know Conway, he found him to be a truly inspiring leader, full of ideas and suggested innovations: some completely impractical, but often containing an idea no one else had thought of. Brainstorming sessions for problem solving were the norm.

> We would have these brainstorming sessions on a Friday afternoon once a month with the design team; just the top people – six of us with Hugh Conway – and go over the things technically that we were doing and what problems we had; and Conway would come up with many ideas. Occasionally he would start you along a track and we would develop something.

> I remember for example at one stage on the missile side we tackled the problem with the *Seacat* that, if the operator takes it down too low, you lose it. It's surface to air, but it does have a surface to surface capability. Hugh Conway said: "What you need is a ball and chain on the back of it. It'll bounce along the crest of the waves and then it'll automatically stay up." Imagine, putting a ball and chain on the back of a missile! But it made us think. From that we developed the miniature altimeter we put into the missile to measure the height above the waves.[4]

Seacat was put on public display for the first time at the Paris Air Show in June 1959. The test vehicle used during the development phase had already been shown at the Farnborough displays of 1957 and 1958, but the finished product attracted widespread interest because of its compact dimensions, cheapness, instant readiness and its stability for warships of modest size. During the 1960s it was to become a brilliant sales success worldwide and won its first Queen's Award to Industry (for technical innovation) in 1967. The paradox was that these achievements coincided with a decade which was to be the most troubled in the company's history and in the course of which its very survival was more than once held in the balance.

Civil aviation was in a state of transition, with the turbo-prop yielding to the new dominance of the pure jet. The much smaller British industry was fighting for its life against the might of American competition. Mounting costs increased the pressures forcing company amalgamations. A number of proud manufacturing names disappeared with the formation of the British Aircraft Corporation and the merger of others. Because of its status as a Government-owned company, Shorts continued to feel uncomfortably exposed to the vagaries of official policy. Castlereagh was not directly involved in the

The *Rackerjack* sorting machine in use at Lilliput Laundry. It was also installed at the GPO.

A DC Defibrillator being demonstrated in the City hospital by Dr Evan Fletcher

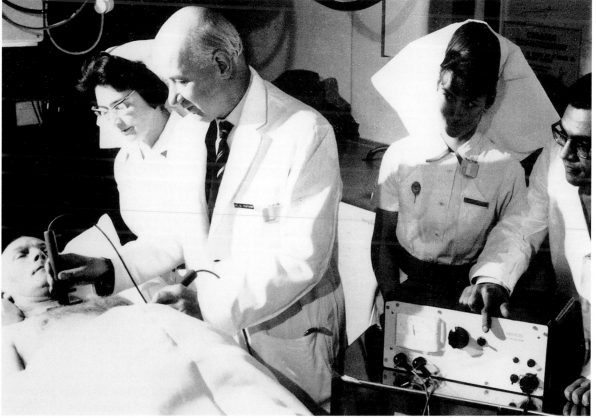

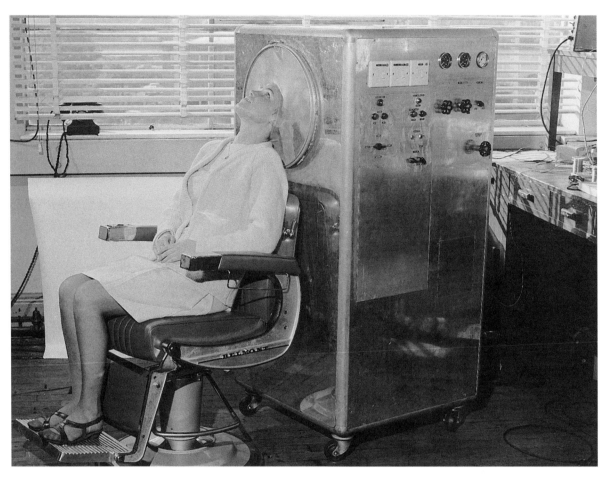

The automatic hair washer and scalp massager developed for René of Mayfair in London

aircraft business. But no one in Guided Weapons entertained any doubts as to its importance. At this time Shorts was employing 8,500 people. If it was to be robbed of its aerostructures activities, which now seemed a real risk, Castlereagh could be forced out on a limb and isolated. The welcome given to *Seacat* promised substantial profitability. But the overheads which have to be absorbed by a small independent company are a vastly greater burden proportionally than those which can be subsumed when it exists beneath the umbrella of a much larger parent. It was not unreasonable that some of the Castlereagh team began to speculate whether Guided Weapons could survive alone.

Due to the risk of being sold off, the company had to diversify. Speculative ventures included laundry sorting machines, hair washers, fencing machinery and medical equipment from DC defibrillators to galvanic skin resistance meters.

As things were, Shorts as a whole was continuing to lose money. By the mid 1960s there was an accumulated deficit, formidable for the time, of £10.4m. In this, of course, the Government was itself heavily implicated. The disastrous contract for the highly complex and very large *Belfast* heavy transport left the company with undischarged development costs of up to £15m. It was wholly responsible for driving Shorts from the black into the red because the Government refused to order more than ten for the RAF. Meantime the rumours from Whitehall were that the Committee appointed in 1964 and headed by Lord Plowden, an industrialist who had spent the war at the Ministry of Aircraft Production, favoured cutting Shorts' labour force in half. The remainder would be diverted into non-aviation activities, with the industry nationally being reduced to two large aircraft builders and one engine manufacturer.

Cuthbert Wrangham, in 1960, at the age of 52, had replaced Slattery as Chairman on the latter's departure to head British Overseas Airways Corporation. Wrangham, although he had been plucked from gas, hotel and insurance boardrooms to head Shorts, had a sound knowledge of the fundamentals of aviation policy, having spent the Second World War, first with the Air Ministry and then, like Plowden, with the new Ministry of Aircraft Production. One day in 1965 he was summoned, with Foreman, to meet the Minister of Aviation, Roy Jenkins, in Whitehall, to be told of the contents of Plowden's report. Jenkins had no background in aviation. Harold Wilson knew the Ministry needed a strong hand, but was at a loss whom to appoint. Jenkins had been chosen a few months before on the strength of a forceful article he had written for *The Observer* on BOAC and the VC10 airliner – which a colleague placed on the Prime Minister's desk.[5] At the meeting Foreman recognised at once that Jenkins was in a state of acute embarrassment –

> We didn't know what was in the report and he didn't know what to say. He sat there. I can see him now, his hands wriggling around. What he was really saying was that there was nowhere for Shorts to go – it's dead. "You know", he said, "that the Plowden report isn't favourable towards you. It says we should only have two groups, two consortia, one Hawker Siddeley and the other the British Aircraft Corporation, and I'm afraid you'll not be included in either of them. Similarly, Handley Page will not be included in either of them."
> What could we say? We protested. But what could you say? The fact is that he did it badly.[6]

In fact Shorts was to weather this storm, though things remained difficult. Although new aerostructures contracts had been obtained from Fokker in the Netherlands and VFW in Germany, the appreciation was spreading that it was now Government policy actively to discourage the placing of further aircraft work with Shorts. At the end of the year, Jenkins visited Germany and was given glowing accounts of how well the co-operation with Shorts was going. So successful was it proving, that the Germans were asking Shorts to co-operate on the building of a small airliner of a size for which they knew there was an assured market.

According to reports from Bonn which began to circulate a few weeks later, however, Jenkins told the Germans that in no circumstances would the Government allow Shorts to do the work. Similar reports from within the industry in America conveyed the same story concerning work for Shorts on the McDonnell Douglas *Phantom II* fighter and the Lockheed C130 transport. These explosive allegations, of which the company had been told nothing, culminated in a prominent headline in *The Times* on 24 January 1966, alleging that the four Government nominees on the Shorts board, three of them high-powered former civil servants with a close professional knowledge of the aircraft industry, were about to resign in protest. Wrangham, though, was determined to tough it out: to stand and fight. So he remained resolute that Shorts was going to remain as a builder of aircraft and missiles. Accordingly, the decision was taken at ministerial level to get rid of the Chairman.

Things came to a head in the Summer of 1967. Brian Faulkner, the energetic Minister of Commerce at Stormont, and the Shorts board, including its four Government-appointed directors, gave Wrangham their unconditional backing. But Wedgwood Benn, now wearing the old aviation hat under the new guise of Minister of Technology, was determined the Chairman had to go. Relations at the top had been worsening for months and it was clear communication between Ministry, and the company for which it was directly responsible, left much to be desired. As things were, the sacking of their Chairman came as a bombshell to the board.

On the morning of 20 June Wrangham's secretary took a call from Chapman Pincher, defence correspondent of the *Daily Express*, at Shorts' London office in Berkeley Square. Wrangham was not available, but Pincher told her he had an important and urgent message. She should advise her boss at once that the Minister of Technology was going to sack him. Alerted by his office, Wrangham, rushed round to see Benn that afternoon. The Minister duly confirmed the accuracy of Pincher's message, but would say no more about the Government's intentions.

An emergency meeting of the board was called for the following afternoon. It emerged that the Chairman, in his dismissal, was paying the price of winning. Government plans had clearly provided for the steady rundown of Shorts as an aircraft and missile builder. When Wrangham refused to entertain the proposed time table, he was told to go. But the crux was that ministers were obliged to think again and Shorts remained as a builder of both aircraft and missiles. Benn told the Commons that the company had a clear programme of aviation work and would be supported by the Government, but the Minister found there were no takers for the chairmanship: it was to remain vacant until the following year with one of the members of the board,

Denis Haviland, serving in an acting capacity.

It was during this period of flux that two important changes occurred in the management of the company. In 1964 that driving spirit who had done so much for Shorts, and particularly for Castlereagh, over the preceding decade, Hugh Conway, resigned as Managing Director to take up the same position at the Bristol Engine Division of Rolls Royce. In the same year, Conway's recruit, Philip Foreman, was appointed company Chief Engineer. Three years later, in 1967, at what was a critical stage, he took over as Managing Director. Shorts had accumulated losses of some £12m. But Foreman expressed himself confident that capital reorganisation would be carried through and that the firm could look forward to a relaxation in the rigidity of Government control. Meantime, Castlereagh was poised to generate badly-needed profits for the company, with a guided weapons man at the helm.

NOTES

1   Sir Philip Foreman: Presidential Address to the *Institution of Mechanical Engineers*, London, 21 October 1985

2   Foreman, op.cit.

3   Do.

4   Foreman, interview with author. The significance of their altimeter was not immediately appreciated by the Ministry of Defence; cf. Chap.11

5   *The Times*, 9 January 2003.

6   Foreman, interview with author

9

The Colonel Shows How

THE international stock market is accurately described as a running contest between fear and greed. In a skittish market, one impulse urges a sale to bank profits, for fear of a fall; but greed applies pressure to hold on in hopes of a further rise. The international arms market is governed by similar characteristics. Defence is a big money business. As such it is under continuous and greedy pressure from the domestic departments in a nation's treasury seeking to contain its voracious demands. Further infighting occurs as the rival services compete for the largest share of the cake. But the defence budget is always a favourite source of economies for finance ministers. The defence lobby counters this by bringing fear into play, working at two levels.

The first is the politically disastrous fate awaiting the prime minister presiding over a nation found wanting when attacked. Stanley Baldwin is remembered, probably a little unfairly, as the Premier in the 1930s who refused to disclose the extent of the nation's belated rearmament plans before the 1935 General Election. He knew the people were in no mood to be roused from their slumbers and, as he rashly admitted afterwards, he feared that he would lose it if he did.

The second level takes the form of the national fear of subjugation and defeat. Chamberlain is reviled as the man who bent the knee to Hitler at Munich in 1938 because he feared the French lacked the will and his own nation the adequate means to fight. In reality, though, the hindsight of history confirms that Hitler was much weaker even than the French alone. When the Fuhrer marched into the Rhineland in 1936 he could have been toppled at a stroke by a single French division. It was Hitler, not Chamberlain, who gained most from the time bought so expensively at Munich. The catastrophic results of the miscalculation re-echo balefully down the years, acting as the most fundamental energiser of the world arms business and being quoted, even into the twenty-first century, as justification for a hawkish United States foreign policy in the Middle East.

Shorts' Guided Weapons Division, like all other armaments makers, was dependent, more or less exclusively, upon the co-operation of

Governments at home and abroad for its sales. The key agency was the Defence Sales Organisation in Whitehall, with its trading offshoot, Millbank Technical Services, lurking in the wings. The Defence Sales Organisation was set up by Denis Healey during his long tenure of the Defence Ministry in the Wilson Government of 1964-70. Sir Philip Foreman acknowledged how closely Shorts worked with this lucrative arm of government –

> We were very close to the Defence Sales Organisation. We didn't go and sell things to anybody without doing it through the Defence Sales Organisation – "There's a ship being built – perhaps you can sell *Seacat.*"This could be anywhere – information coming from the attaches round the world. They were very helpful: that was their job. Because of the political considerations, we never sold anything without it going through the Organisation.[2]

With this in mind it was natural enough for armaments suppliers to equip themselves with a sales force fluent in the language and thinking of their potential clients. Basically this meant ex-officers. In the services they had been used to lives of constant postings and frequent travel. On the normal early military retirement and with a gratuity in the bank, a globetrotting sales job at Shorts had obvious attractions.[3] Commander Keith Burnett joined the *Seacat* technical sales team in the early days in 1958 after 27 years in the Royal Navy. Subsequently he was to make three round-the-world trips.

The company's missile sales, by the late 1960s were running in a typical year at the rate of some £1m. a month, with *Seacat* already in the service of 13 countries worldwide. With inflated prices in the intervening years, this was a much more considerable achievement than it might appear at first sight today. A rain check on 1967, for example, a year when Castlereagh sold £5m. worth of guided weapons to Iran and Argentina alone, shows that the weekly expenditure on food for an average British family was £6 7s. 5d - the equivalent of £6.37p. Rent and rates accounted for a mere £2.26, the mortgage for a modest £1.96, fuel for £1.46 and drink for a memorable 98p.[4]

Missile sales were already headed by a former Royal Navy man, Commander Peter Hill. The company now drew upon the Royal Marines for Major Hugh Orpen, appointed Assistant Sales Manager in 1969 after a wartime career with the Commandos in the Middle and Far East and service in the Caribbean and Central America. Flight Lieutenant Norman Wright, appointed Sales Engineer, had seven years' experience evaluating the *Red Top* air-to-air missile at Woomera and Boscombe Down for the RAF. The full circle of the services was to be completed in 1972 when Brigadier Peter Gwynne-Lewis, an Army ordnance expert, joined the missile sales team.

In the early days the team was not without its flamboyant side. Colonel Stevens undoubtedly provided part of it. He had spent some years in the old colonial service in West Africa and was recruited to exploit possibilities there. He arrived at Castlereagh in a very large Rolls Royce safari car, equipped with every available item of survival gear for long-distance desert journeys, including a shovel strapped to the tailgate. Later, when the Colonel had got into his stride, the chief cashier's curiosity was aroused by a notable idiosyncrasy in the gentleman's travels: all his overseas journeys included a call at the Black Forest spa of Baden-Baden. But, as the cashier failed to establish that these frequent calls were either costing the company any extra money or restricting the Colonel's calls on overseas customers, management did not intervene. It later transpired that he had a woman friend of means in the resort in question. Martin Armour had his first direct contact with the Colonel during an abortive sales visit to Switzerland –

I and my sales representative and my weapons system engineer flew to Zurich and made our way by the magnificent Swiss railway system to Berne, where we arrived in the evening, a Sunday. Our first task was to order a drink from room service. Minutes passed, more minutes passed and no sign of room service. At this point the Colonel arrived fresh from Baden-Baden.

On being told that drinks were desired but room service was failing to respond, the Colonel at once took over.

He got on the phone and when it was eventually answered said: "Hier sprechen Herr Oberstleutnant Stevens" and I swear you could hear the heels click at the far end of the phone. Within minutes our drinks were on the table.

We had a friend with us from a firm which specialised in radar and he said to the Colonel, "What special power do you have over bartenders?" The Colonel explained that a military rank carried much influence in most European countries. Then our radar friend said, "I must remember that. What is the German equivalent of my rank? I was a second lieutenant." The Colonel looked, as I thought, rather pityingly at our friend and said,

"I don't think that your rank of leutnant will impress the German-speaking Europeans, any more than second lieutenant will impress the rank and file of the British Army".[5]

Although military attachés at British embassies abroad were there largely to further the sales of British armaments and were often of great help to Shorts, there could be difficulties. Whether this had anything to do with the fact that the company was based in Ireland, albeit the British part, it is impossible to say. But, leaving the hotel with slow room service the next morning for the British embassy in Berne, things did not go smoothly. The team's first task was to collect their photographic slides and documents which, because they were classified, had to be conveyed in the diplomatic bag.

A sales colleague had warned Armour not to expect a warm reception. Having had difficulty before in getting through the front door, he had devised an alternative strategy in this and other foreign capitals. Having arranged an appointment for the Monday, he would turn up at the English church on Sunday morning. Being a presentable person who readily facilitated conversation, he usually succeeded in being invited to lunch by one of the ladies on the Embassy staff. But the salesman's ruse did not always work as planned; and Martin Armour's mission in Berne was one example –

> He had been invited for lunch in Berne, but he must have picked the wrong official; for when we met the military attaché to collect our papers we were looked upon as arms peddlers and sent packing with no advice or offer of assistance. I was appalled, as about 200 yards away was the United States Embassy with 200 technical personnel specifically designated to sell US weapons, from police revolvers to tanks and bomber aircraft.[6]

They did meet a high-powered team from the Swiss defence forces, but came away empty handed, selling nothing.

The Germans also proved a difficult nut to crack with a sale of *Seacat* to the Navy. Prospects appeared good; for the West Germans, post-war, were reconstructing their fleet largely with an eye to operations in the shallow Baltic Sea. This produced plans for fast and highly manoeuvrable vessels with sophisticated anti-aircraft armament, but with range and ocean seaworthiness lesser considerations. *Seacat* would clearly be of interest; and so it proved. In fact the Germans were to spend a great deal of money evaluating the missile, buying a number of *Seacats* and submitting them to the most rigorous tests under the most severe climatic conditions. They even experimented to satisfy themselves that, if a missile failed to launch on deck, the flaming exhaust from the rocket motor would not set fire to the ship. They also fitted a guided missile patrol boat with a complete *Seacat* system and sailed it to the Aberporth guided missile range on Cardigan Bay in Wales for test firings against towed targets. As always, the resilience of Murphy's Law was to be proven, even to the Germans –

> Just before the completion of the series a trial was in progress in which the *Seacat* aimer had the towed target firmly in his sights and was awaiting instruction to fire. As the instruction was given, the towed target fouled the tow-rope and went into an uncontrolled spin. By this time the missile was on its way and to everyone's consternation the aimer directed it against the tug. The result was a very expensive radio-controlled aircraft vaporised in a ball of flame. The cheers of the *Seacat* trials team watching from the shore could be heard in Cardigan.[7]

The drone destroyed in this trial was of a type developed by the Australian Government for use on the Woomera test range and cost about £250,000. So the Germans cut short their trials at Aberporth, but, with typical thoroughness, decided to pursue their testing of *Seacat* at their Baltic research station at Surendorf, where they had a hydraulic rolling platform used to test naval guns under simulated high seas conditions. After the trials the *Seacat* marketing team was invited to attend the final conference to hear the verdict. The Germans spoke good English and had been to Castlereagh frequently; but it was explained to the Shorts visitors on this occasion that, under Government regulations, the proceedings had to be conducted in German. This was to involve the usual disputes with the rival interpreters over the rendering of technical terms and there was much waving of arms from the Germans who spoke English. But the Shorts team had a smattering of the language, having assiduously worked after hours in the Castlereagh canteen in an evening class organised for the purpose. So Martin Armour was able to make a ten-minute speech in German at the farewell dinner.

But the Federal Navy in the end resolved to rely on 3in guns for anti-aircraft armament as back-up for the *Exocet* ship-to-ship missiles and long-range guided torpedoes on its fast patrol boats in the Baltic; and upon *Harpoon* ship-to-air and *Sea Sparrow* ship-to-ship missiles on its 12 Type-122 frigates. This was a disappointment for Shorts: but all was not lost. Even if they did not in the end become clients, the Germans were deeply interested in the *Seacat* technology. They would not have invested so much money in testing it if they had not. Worldwide, this was of great importance; for German scientists, thanks to the disproportionate extent of the resources devoted to missile technology by Hitler in the later stages of the Second World War, were acknowledged to be leaders in the science. The Castlereagh team had gone to great lengths to cultivate their contacts with the Federal German Navy. Their reward was positive German approval for *Seacat* which was a most influential asset in future sales elsewhere abroad.

Shorts' technological advance at Castlereagh also aroused interest nearer home. British Aerospace, Shorts' major domestic competitor, was watching the success of *Seacat* from its own missile base at Stevenage in Hertfordshire. In reality it was not a direct rival, for it had no established close-range weapon of its own; and, as it noted the sales of *Seacat* to navies worldwide through the 1960s, its designers and market planners could have been excused had they wondered if they had failed to back the winning horse.

Outside interest in the clear potential of Castlereagh was also increased by uncertainty over the future of Shorts itself. The difficulties in relations between the board and the Government in the late 1960s fed this atmosphere. Things came to a head following the decision of the RAF, supported by the Government, not to order more than ten of the big Belfast transports, and to order its American rival instead. Hopes of export sales were still-born and the company was left with a massive debt from undischarged development costs. As a result, the newly-appointed Managing Director, Philip Foreman, barred by Shorts' status as a Government-owned enterprise from borrowing in the market, was heavily preoccupied with a looming financial crisis.

One result was that at Castlereagh, Armour, who had taken over from Foreman as General Manager of Guided Weapons, found himself very much left alone to get on with the job. In fact Castlereagh, busy by this time turning out hundreds of missile rounds a week in projects providing jobs for 1,500 people, had been developing almost as a self-sufficient entity. The factory and research department had little day to day contact with the main plant at Queen's Island beyond making use of its central services for security and vehicle maintenance. It was at this juncture that Armour was warned, in a telephone call from Foreman, not to float the factory off and make a unilateral declaration of independence! Because, his MD went on, English Electric had their eye on them and were just waiting to make a bid to take over Castlereagh as a separate unit.[8]

This reference to an outside predator was only half in jest. Armour was shortly to receive an invitation to visit the British Aerospace missile plant at Stevenage. There he was wined and dined, but in the course of the hospitality was subjected to a regimen of searching questions. What was Shorts' sales policy? What was their chosen path into contacts with Government? But the real interest of BAe was in Shorts' success in the close-range missile market which in the late 1960s, Shorts had shown in spectacular fashion, was wide open to exploitation. British Aerospace suggested to Armour that, with Shorts' expertise in close-range ship-to-air and theirs with automatic guidance on *Rapier* and *Sea Wolf*, the two companies could collaborate to mutual benefit on a new product. They anticipated - correctly – that Shorts would develop a surface-to-air version of *Seacat* and were clearly attempting to climb on board.[9]

Castlereagh, though, was making profits and had ample plans of its own for the future. *Seacat* was soon to be built into the most widely sold shipboard missile. Probably the most important factor after its proven design was its comparitively modest cost. It was essential to its success that so many navies could afford it. A big advantage was its status as an add-on, capable of being fitted to existing vessels without major refit. When the new breed of frigates, fast and lightweight, became popular in so many navies, Shorts designed a lightweight marque of the *Seacat* launcher to meet the naval architects' demand that top weight be kept down.

But Shorts' design team was itself a focus of interest. The Castlereagh team had been built from nothing; for, as Foreman explained-

> When we began there were very few electronic engineers in Northern Ireland. We had to get them trained. So we built up a very capable team at Castlereagh. The engineering design team was probably about a hundred strong altogether. But these electronic engineers were like gold dust. And you couldn't stop them leaving. A lot had left and gone into other places in Northern Ireland who were starting up and looking for people - not to do missiles, but to do just straightforward precision electronic work. They recruited from us. We were a pool of desirable labour.[10]

Informal contact between the missile companies also fed the traffic in highly-prized electronic engineers. Castlereagh lost one to a London

Some of the original team in the Precision Engineering Division with the *Seacat* missile. From left, Martin Armour, Rex Galway, Jim Foye, Wally Galloway, Peter Hill, Reg Harriman, Dick Ransom, Fred Lowens, Billy Turner (kneeling), Phil Foreman, David Kennedy (kneeling)

manufacturer, another to a professorial chair in Bangor, North Wales, a third to a manufacturer of mechanical aids for polio victims, a fourth to Armstrong Whitworth's missile division and a fifth, John Seeley, went to British Aerospace. To redress the balance, Castlereagh recruited two of BAe's leading engineers from Stevenage, Charles Raitt-Brown and Terry Stone. They joined an expanding team poised to build on the success of *Seacat*.

NOTES

1 John Terraine, op.cit; pp53–70

2 Foreman, interview with author

3 Cf. also Chap. 14

4 Ministry of Labour Family Expenditure Survey, 1967

5 Armour, op.cit., p139

6 Armour, op.cit., p140.

7 Armour, op.cit., p141

8 Armour, op.cit., p167

9 Armour, interview with author

10 Foreman, interview with author

10

MIDNIGHT IN MOSCOW

The arrival of *Seacat* on the international scene as a key player in the business of ship-to-air guided weapons attracted widespread attention in the defence industry and among its clients. But the Cold War was at its height in the early 1960s. In the West reds were in danger of being spotted under every bed. Le Carré was putting the finishing touches to his classic tale, *The Spy who Came in from the Cold*. Kim Philby, lately an officer in British Intelligence, but also a double agent, was about to defect. It was the age of Smiley, the building of the Berlin Wall and of espionage films which all seemed to begin at the notorious Checkpoint Charlie. In such an international climate it was the most natural thing in the world that potential enemies, as well as bona fide clients, would be interested in what Shorts' scientists and missile engineers were doing.

Because of the Government's direct involvement, the Castlereagh plant was visited regularly by teams of officials from Whitehall. The old War Office, the Admiralty and the Ministry of Aviation were all interested in the missile business. All three, or their successors, eventually were to be clients of Shorts. So visits by officials attracted little notice. But, seen in retrospect, such routine comings and goings were the perfect cover for an eavesdropper who wished to find out with detail and precision how far the weapons work had progressed.

Frank Clifton Bossard is recalled by the older hands among the Castlereagh technical team by name only. Most of those who were there at the time he used to visit the plant can give scant description of what he looked like. The early 1960s are a long time ago, but the vagueness of most of those who met Bossard is not without significance. "A grey man" said one. "Just like any of those visiting civil servants," said another. "A man in a suit."

This only proves that Bossard knew his business. As a Soviet agent, his first responsibility was to merge into the woodwork, keep eyes and ears open and, above all, attract no undue personal attention to himself. But among the senior personnel at Castlereagh, one manager preserved a more precise memory. George Townend is a perceptive Yorkshireman from Brough in the old North Riding. He had come to

Belfast in 1948 to take a draughtsman's job at Shorts, moved to Castlereagh when it opened in 1952 and subsequently became Project Manager on the *Javelin* missile and later overall Project Manager of the company's armoury of guided weapons.

He recalled meetings with Bossard on the development of *Seacat*, one of which the civil servant chaired at the Aviation Ministry in London. Townend remembered him as a dour individual, about fifty, tall and well built, grey-haired and balding, and fond of his pipe. In fact the spy was another Yorkshireman, born on 13 December 1912 at Great Driffield near Bridlington in the old East Riding, the son of a joiner who died a few weeks before his birth. His mother remarried, this time to a farm worker at Gedney in Lincolnshire.

Bossard was an ambitious youngster, but his mother and his stepfather, George Lester, lacked the means to send him to grammar school and he was obliged to leave the village school when he turned 14. It was while working in a cycle and radio shop in the early 1930s that he discovered an intense interest in wireless and enrolled for a technical college course. He was also fascinated by Nazi Germany and joined Sir Oswald Mosley's British Union of Fascists. The anti-communism of the eloquent Mosley attracted considerable numbers of the better off and, by the time he was 21, Bossard had succeeded in losing his provincial north country accent. But his wages as a shop worker were not enough to allow him to keep up socially with his new acquaintances. He began to bounce cheques, was caught and sentenced to six months in gaol.

Shortly after the outbreak of war he joined the RAF, applying for a commission with a supporting, but invented, curriculum vitae to match his newly cultivated accent. It omitted his prison record but included a public school education and a diploma in radio. He left the Air Force radar branch in March 1946 as a 33-year-old flight lieutenant. In the next few years he got married, held a lectureship at the Air Services College at Hamble, near Portsmouth, and in 1951 got a job as a signals officer at the Ministry of Civil Aviation.

It was five years later that he was transferred to the Intelligence bureau at the Ministry of Defence and sent as an attaché to the British Embassy in Bonn. Among his duties was the screening of scientists and engineers who had got out of East Germany. Aided by an ample entertainment allowance, he grew knowledgeable about developments in guided weapons behind the Iron Curtain, and seems to have had an affair with the rich and attractive wife of a Berlin businessman. But he also tended to drink too much, something which must have been noted by the Soviet agents who would have been planted among the genuine refugees. In fact after being posted back to England in 1958 to head the Intelligence bureau at the Ministry of Defence, he was approached one lunchtime in a London pub by a man who said his name was Gordon and appeared to know the nature of his work.

Bossard was missing the tax-free extra allowances he had had in Germany; his salary had been virtually halved by the home posting; he had a large mortgage on his Surrey house and school fees for his son. Once again he was not only short of cash but heavily in debt.

After several similarly casual encounters, Gordon admitted that he was on the staff of the Russian embassy and would pay well for the right kind of information. As an earnest of the future, during an exchange in a room at the George Hotel in Holland Park, he offered the Ministry man two hundred pounds in five pound notes. For Bossard this represented more than a month's salary before tax. He was in no position to refuse and he agreed to work for the Russians. At the beginning of 1960, when *Seacat* was being seriously evaluated with a view to the placing of its first production contract, Bossard was moved from Defence to Aviation, attached to the naval guided weapons branch. In his new post he was among the few civil servants cleared to visit the top secret firing range at Aberporth where *Seacat* was first tested. He could not have been much closer to the Navy's unique new missile.

Bossard, though, when he began to work for his new masters, suffered from one grave difficulty. The common office photocopier was an invention still a decade away and the fax machine even further. Like all undercover agents of the time purloining secret documents, he was obliged to operate in the manner of Elyesa Bazna, the Turkish valet of the British Ambassador to Ankara during the Second World War. The celebrated "Cicero" stole the keys to his master's safe and had duplicates made. He then removed selected documents (including the Allied plans for the invasion of Normandy), photographing them in his room with a Leica lit by a one hundred watt bulb, and selling the prints to the incredulous Germans over twelve months in 1943 and 1944.

On a Friday Bossard would go to the old Ivanhoe Hotel, a modest, staid and suitably quiet hostelry in Bloomsbury, round the corner from the Ministry offices on New Oxford Street. There he would book a room for the following Monday in the name of J. Hathaway. At lunchtime on that day he would leave his office with the classified documents in his brief case, going to the left-luggage depository at Waterloo and collecting the suitcase in which he kept his camera, films and a stand to support the documents. It was but a short taxi ride to the hotel. His operation there, using an East German *Praktika* 35mm camera with a through-the-lens viewfinder ideal for his close-up task, took but a few minutes.

But Bossard's comings and goings had aroused suspicion. He was put under close surveillance by MI5 three months before the Scotland Yard special branch swooped. But the Ministry man was clever enough to prevent them nailing any other member of the extensive Soviet espionage network with whom he collaborated.

The nature of his contact proved to be straight out of Le Carré.

The 35mm films of the Ministry documents were delivered through a series of nine dead-letter boxes in quiet residential districts in the Home Counties – at Blackheath, at a broken drain pipe on an estate in Weybridge, or at a particular birch tree by a pathway at Woking or a beech tree earmarked at Leatherhead. Bossard received his payment in bank notes through the same drops and also his further instructions, which were printed microscopically on 35mm film, to be read with a magnifying glass.

In the kitchen at his home in Stoke d'Abernon near Cobham he kept a sophisticated radio communications set and headphones in the kitchen, which he explained away to his wife as essential for his work for British Intelligence. Bossard was under orders to listen to Radio Moscow at fixed times, early morning and mid-evening, when one of five well known tunes would be played.[1] Each represented a coded message. He bought records of them to make recognition sure. One was the *Song of the Volga Boatmen*. Another was from *Swan Lake*, a third from *Kalinka*, a fourth the *Sabre Dance*; the last, *Midnight in Moscow*, was what he usually heard. It meant he should continue operations as before.

The Russians never copied *Seacat* or *Tigercat*, but there is every reason to believe that Bossard furnished them with every detail of their unique design. The propulsion and guidance systems, which were both ingenious and at the same time simple in concept, may well have had a useful application elsewhere in the extensive Soviet armoury. In any case the thirteenth department of the first chief directorate of the KGB, responsible for contact with agents abroad and for which Bossard worked, would have attached high value to this access to the thinking behind the enemy weaponry they might face, should the Cold War once again threaten to become hot.

Bossard pleaded guilty to charges of espionage at the Old Bailey on 10 May 1965. The Lord Chief Justice, Lord Parker, sent him down for twenty-one years, observing that the sentence would have been even longer had not the prisoner made a full confession.

What was carefully suppressed at his trial and remained unknown to those who wrote the accounts published after it, was how he had been caught. Although already a suspect, the security men had to catch their quarry at large outside the office with the booty. This was not easy. They never saw him with any of his Russian contacts. How they did it did not emerge until the embargo on relevant documents was lifted many years later.

The nature of the method explains the official reluctance. Like the Edwardian murderer, Dr. Crippen, arrested on board ship in 1910 by the first use of wireless in a murder hunt, Bossard was trapped by new means. Suitably, in view of the nature of the intelligence which was the subject of his treachery, he was the first spy to be caught by the now-familiar, but then very novel, instrument, the electronic bleeper.

Several of these miniature transmitters were secretly fitted to the metal clips securing classified files which it was reckoned would attract Bossard's interest. They were then routed to his desk. When, on 15 March 1964, he took the bait and left the Ministry at lunchtime with the documents in his briefcase, the bleepers transmitted their signals and he was followed to the hotel by the special branch.[2]

They saw him enter a second-floor room just before one o'clock and settled down to wait. He emerged an hour and a half later and was cautioned and searched. His briefcase was found to contain four files marked secret. The suitcase contained the camera and spare films, as well as the document stand and the records of the pieces of Russian music. He also had four exposed rolls of film, a magnifying glass and a list of the locations of the dead letter boxes.

In his confession, Bossard told the police: "I selected files on guided weapons".[3]

NOTES

1 Norman Lucas: *The Great Spy Ring* (London, 1966) contains a detailed account of the Bossard case, pp253-261

2 John Barron: *The KGB* (London, 1974), p80

3 Chapman Pincher: *Inside Story* (London, 1979), p 151

11

TIGERCAT

THE success of *Seacat* was such that, by the late 1960s, Shorts was well on the way to achieving its unique status as the manufacturer of the world's most widely-sold guided weapons system. A policy of constant improvement was important. As sales grew, the demands of new customers were a constant spur to innovation. Notably, a lightweight three-round launcher appeared in 1969; though, as explained below, this emerged from an inquiry from the Royal Air Force, not the Navy. But the new launcher weighed only half as much as the standard four-round system already in service with 14 navies worldwide. It meant that for the first time small naval craft and inshore minesweepers could be equipped with their own guided missile defence and there was a successful first live firing on the Solent in the autumn.

Another innovation was the substitution of transistors for the bulky, old (and much less dependable) thermionic valves. The immediate gain was a big reduction in the weight and size of the battery required. In turn this also made vacant space available which was exploited to increase the size of the warhead. Thus was *Seacat* Mod I born.

It was important for Shorts that the progress and increasing sophistication of *Seacat* had not gone unnoticed at home any more than it had abroad. One interested and influential spectator was Air Chief Marshal Sir Philip Joubert de la Ferte, Commandant of the RAF Regiment, the militia whose responsibility it was to defend the service's air bases worldwide. Joubert knew all about Shorts. He had been Commander-in-Chief of RAF Coastal Command in 1941 during the top-level tussle in Whitehall over whether the Belfast factory should be producing more *Sunderland* flying boats (to chase U-Boats in the Atlantic) or more *Stirlings* (to bomb Germany). In addition his airfields were still using the 40mm guns for anti-aircraft defence which *Seacat* was replacing in the Royal Navy and in fourteen navies abroad. He came to the commonsense conclusion that what was good enough for the Navy might also be good enough for him; and so he resolved to pay a visit to Belfast.

Opposite: Seacat missiles ready for dispatch to customers

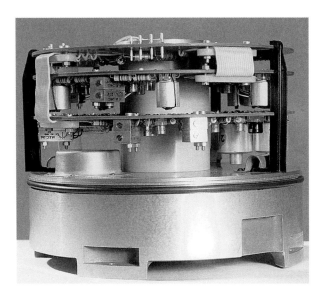 

The thermionic valve guidance pack (right) and the much smaller transistorised electronic pack (above)

This proved to be an event of great importance. Shorts had already been thinking of a land-based version of *Seacat*. When Joubert laid his cards on the table at Castlereagh, it was immediately obvious that there was no reason why a surface-to-air marque could not be readily adapted. Indeed, with the aimer positioned on terra firma, his task would be a great deal easier than it was on the rolling deck of a warship. All that was necessary was a launcher unit fixed to a wheeled chassis. Shorts broached the idea of a trailer unit, incorporating a director and launcher and towed by a Land Rover to the Ministry of Defence. The Castlereagh team pointed to the obvious export potential and proposed a Government development contract. But, as so often proved to be the case when a new idea was floated, officials at the Ministry showed faint enthusiasm. So Castlereagh passed the depressing news to the Air Marshal that they had "run into a stone wall". Joubert's reaction was to advise the design team to go ahead: he would look after the Ministry.

Castlereagh had no idea how he proposed to do it. But the Air Marshal was a formidable and determined individual. He had begun his service in the First World War in the Artillery and ended it as a pilot in the new RAF – with a DSO, six mentions in despatches and decorations from both the French and the Italian governments. He was not to be put off. Joubert clearly knew how to open doors - and the Ministry was duly to confess defeat.

Shorts in the meantime had indeed forged ahead. When the derivative design was ready, with a new launcher light enough to be supported on a wheeled chassis, a development contract covering six of the new sets was awarded. This was absolutely vital to further advance. The development costs were ruinously expensive and not feasible to incur without a reasonable prospect of a commercial return. But, with the RAF Regiment now on board, Castlereagh celebrated by naming its new defensive weapon *Tigercat*. A first firing was successfully accomplished at the Aberporth range shortly before Christmas 1967. A few months later an RAF Regiment team moved in for a two-week exercise in which the new missile was deployed round the airfield adjacent to Shorts' complex at Sydenham (now Belfast City Airport).

Tigercat test firing by the Royal Air Force

The RAF *Tigercat* Fire Unit
deployed ready for action

The Air Force contract represented a major vote of confidence and Tigercat immediately attracted interest abroad. *Seacat* customers, and the service departments of other nations who sent delegates to the big international arms shows, appreciated at once the advantages of a weapon which made available to land forces the established naval advantages of Seacat – cheapness, adaptability and comparative simplicity.

The Government's Defence Sales Organisation in Whitehall at this time was flexing its muscles. In 1969 Sir Ray Brown had been succeeded as Head of Defence Sales by Lester Suffield, a wartime major in the RASC whose peacetime background was in selling cars, much of it in North America. He came to the Ministry as the 58-year-old retired Sales Director of British Leyland and regarded selling arms as just the same as the job he had once done for Morris Motors. His was an enthusiastic and outspoken approach, one inclined to draw the occasional sniffy remark from traditionalists among the generals and admirals, not to mention the air marshals, sitting at Ministry desks. But they knew arms sales were doing well, producing revenue of hundreds of millions a year. (Suffield was to be knighted in 1973.) In Whitehall they were used to conducting visitors round the Ministry's permanent exhibition of British weapons for sale. There Shorts' weapons took their place in one corner, neatly propped up on a bed of gravel, among what Suffield facetiously called "the naughty stuff" – machine guns, mortars and missiles. They also knew the proceeds were helping to pay for their own hardware and services personnel; so mostly the brass swallowed their pride.[1]

The chronicler of arms sales, however, soon finds that the precise dimensions of the proceeds are carefully guarded secrets. Selling arms, saving Sir Leslie's enthusiasm, is a sensitive business – both for the supplier and the client. There are no official figures issued of British sales to individual countries. Journalists' inquiries are parried by press officers, each of whom has signed the Official Secrets Act and who advise that the details of all transactions are confidential. Politicians who inquire are regarded as troublemakers seeking ammunition, if of a figurative nature, for use in hostile interventions in the House of Commons. So only the most rounded approximations of Shorts' missile sales are extant. When the house magazine, *Short Story*, detailed the output of missile components at Castlereagh, those components of which only one was fitted to each missile were omitted. To include them would have given too close an indication of factory output.

On occasion orders taken are announced without the name of the customer being disclosed, notably in the case of deals in South America. From time to time this suits one or both sides. The client government may wish to conceal from its neighbours the extent of its rearming; or the manufacturer may feel vulnerable to domestic attack for supplying a foreign government of dubious democracy. In fact the navies of Argentina, Brazil, Chile and Venezuela were all operating *Seacat* in the 1960s without a specific public announcement ever having been made.

The unusually close relationship between British arms manufacturers and the Ministry of Defence encourages secrecy merely because it facilitates it. As a rule all the vital decisions are taken behind the scenes. Parliament may impose an arms embargo, but it is the officials at Defence who will interpret and apply it. MPs will know nothing of the discussions in Whitehall other than what they can ferret out on their own investigation.

The biggest market for British arms undoubtedly is in the Middle East. Oil wealth means the producing states can not only pay their bills on time; it means they can also afford the best. None in the 1960s and 1970s was more demanding than the Shah of Iran. When Shorts was establishing itself as a serious player in the post-war international arms business, Iran was pre-eminent, accounting, according to one study, for fully sixty per cent of the Middle East arms market in the mid-1970s. In one case (in 1976), *Rapier* missiles from

The lightweight *Seacat* system being fired from the Iranian ship Artemis

the British Aircraft Corporation were actually swapped directly for Iranian oil.[2] First *Seacat*, and then *Tigercat*, were to attract the interest of the Shah.

In 1967 he authorised contracts with Shorts for the fitting of *Seacat* to five ships of the Imperial Navy and *Tigercat* for the Imperial Air Force for the defence of airfields and military bases. Seacat was already the standard British naval close-range air defence weapon. *Tigercat* had been selected by the RAF Regiment. Endorsement by the home defence forces was the essential base for expanding export sales. Once achieved, the effect on exports could be dramatic. By 1967 *Seacat* was fitted to all kinds of craft from small patrol boats to aircraft carriers. Its list of export clients included Sweden, the Netherlands, West Germany, Australia, New Zealand, India, Malaysia as well as the South American states already mentioned.

Tigercat meantime had been accepted into service with the Jordanian Army and also in the Gulf state of Qatar; and in November 1970 the Argentinian Army staged its first operational *Tigercat* firing at their Santa Clara army base and artillery range near the east coast city of Mar del Plata. They were also linking *Seacat* to a new fire management system on their 14,000-ton cruiser, *General Belgrano*, to provide integrated control of both the launcher and the ship's guns.[3]

Selling missiles in some respects was very like selling any other sophisticated engineering product. If it had the unique qualities possessed by Shorts' missiles, the price fixed would be influenced by what it was reckoned the client would bear. As sales mounted and the manufacturing unit cost came down, prices generally could be shaved as an incentive. As a client boosted his order, his unit price would be trimmed accordingly. But the early 1970s were years of steeply rising prices, largely driven by the upward spiral of Middle Eastern oil: at one stage the annual increase in the retail price index in the United Kingdom reached the astonishing figure of 28 per cent. The symmetry of this for Shorts, though, was to be found in the fact that, even if its products perforce were growing more expensive, the treasuries of several of its most valuable clients were heavily in pocket from inflated oil revenues. Tensions in the zone ran high, providing the incentive to rearm with the latest technology – and they could afford to spend.

Selling the missiles, in effect, amounted to selling a package. The *Seacat* itself left Castlereagh in an incomplete, knock-down state. The first *Seacats* sold to the Royal Navy were assembled by one or other of their armament depots in bases like Portsmouth and Devonport. Their main task was to assemble shells. They were used to handling explosives. Their engineers now came to Castlereagh to learn how to assemble a missile, how to handle the test equipment once the job was done, pack the product and finally install it on board ship.

Overseas sales involved setting up an armament depot in most of the client countries where on-the-job training could be provided and Shorts engineers could supervise the early practice firings. These were always tense moments. The *Seacat* has a four-barrel launcher: four rounds can be fired before it is necessary to reload. But the launcher requires a director to guide it to the target. George Jackson explained that this raises an obvious problem –

> If you've the director here and the launcher beside it there and you point the director at the target, you can't point the launcher in the same direction – at the same elevation and on the same bearing – because they'll never converge. The other thing is that, if the ship's steaming into the wind, you can have anything up to thirty, forty or fifty knots blowing and this means the missile turns into the wind, going off on its own.[4]

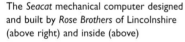
The *Seacat* mechanical computer designed
and built by *Rose Brothers* of Lincolnshire
(above right) and inside (above)

These obvious complications were solved by means of close collaboration with Rose Brothers, the Lincolnshire engineers, on the design of the launcher. They designed an ingenious electro-mechanical computer, which fed in the necessary corrections to the missile's launching trajectory.

When *Seacat* began to sell in large quantities overseas, new demands were created. Handbooks had to be translated, with particular care over technical terms. The client, after all, was going to be handling explosives. The company had its training school at Queen's Island which looked after the familiarisation of foreign aircrew and maintenance engineers with Shorts' aircraft. But when *Seacat* and *Tigercat* started to sell abroad, it became impracticable for the small technical team at Castlereagh to handle its training needs in-house. This was another reason why the training job was done overseas. In effect, aircraft instructors from the training school were given conversion courses to equip them for the missile side, and some new engineers were recruited. While the Castlereagh technical team was supervising installation of the new hardware in the field, an instructor would look after the training of the servicemen who would maintain and operate it.

George Jackson spent three and a half years as Shorts' Resident Engineer in Iran in the late 1960s and early' 70s. His experience underlines how each overseas market demanded its own unique approach if the company was to sustain a satisfactory relationship. In the case of Iran this involved operating in a dictatorship where the regime was under challenge from both within and without and where dissidents suffered arbitrary imprisonment or, not infrequently, execution. In 1980, after years of tension, the eight-year war was to break out with Iraq.

The Iranians had a chain of defensive airfields along their eastern border with Iraq. It was these they wished to equip with close-range missiles. The Shah knew *Tigercat* was coming, but was unwilling to wait for it; so he asked Shorts to install *Seacat* at the two major air bases - three systems at each, with a blockhouse, director and launcher, just as on board ship. Later, 26 *Tigercat* units were delivered to an assembly depot which had been opened in Teheran. A force of ex-service engineers was trained on *Tigercat* in Belfast and based at the Iranian airfields for the next five years to supervise deployment and maintenance.

Although Iran was not a democracy, Jackson recalls his years there not without pleasure –

> You could travel all over the country. I used to take my wife. We'd go off to visit these airfields without any problem. You could stay in a village, stop and buy bread. In those days the Shah was doing a lot for the country. He had conscription, which I don't think particularly was a bad thing. The more educated people, instead of being conscripted into the services were placed in an education corps. They went round and set up schools in all the villages. It was very go-ahead in that respect.

> But it was very much a dictatorship. The Savak secret police were everywhere. In fact one of my engineers at Tabriz, in Azerbaijan, in the north, towards the Russian frontier, had too much to drink one night. The first I heard of it, the General called me into his office. "You have a man up at Tabriz? Get him out of the country."

> I found out this fellow had been drinking the night before and he'd said something about the Shah, which wasn't the brightest thing for anybody to do. I went down to the Embassy and I told the Air Attaché what had happened. He said, "Get him out." So he was on a BOAC plane back to the UK that night. The Savak had reported back what he'd said. That was the other side of the coin.[5]

Technically, despite the most careful preparation, things did go wrong. Embarrassingly, some of the earlier missile sets exported developed a serious transmitter fault: the transmitter would go off the air when the missile was fired. As the firing culminated in a near-explosion, perhaps this was not entirely surprising. Even when things went according to plan, the sequence was not without its drama. There is no actual recoil from the launcher; but it has a hole through which the gases from the motor are expelled under pressure. The end of the motor casing is protected by a six-inch-diameter alloy disc. When the motor is fired, the disc comes off with a forceful thump, to be caught with a loud rattling vibration by a chainmail catcher fitted for the purpose.

So this was the nature of the preliminary to the worst humiliation to be visited upon Jackson's team. In the audience was the top brass of the Iranian services, assembled, in a desert temperature of more than 100 degrees Fahrenheit, for a *Tigercat* demonstration. The site was a range sixty miles south of Teheran on the edge of the salt desert of Dasht-e Kavir one day in 1969 –

> They were all there at this demonstration. The Shah wasn't, but his brother-in-law was. Off went the missile – and dug a big hole in the sand. So we fired another one and the same thing happened. We had an American there from Northrop doing the target aircraft and he turned to me and said. "George, those are the most expensive post hole diggers I've ever seen!" Talk about embarrassment.[6]

Worse was to come for the Iranians: this time off the Dorset coast. It was a Friday evening and Martin Armour had just arrived home when the telephone rang. It was the Resident Engineer in Weymouth who was looking after an Iranian frigate, just delivered from Vosper's in Southampton and on which the new lightweight *Seacat* launcher had just been installed. The Iranians had fired two missiles, but neither had responded to the guidance signals from the director. There was no one at Castlereagh at that hour on a Friday and rather than waste time trying to round up a technical team, Armour resolved to rush over himself –

> I got to the Portland Dockyard, where the ship was based, around lunchtime on Saturday. The ship was at sea with two of our service engineers on board, trying to find the problem. I went on board about six o'clock when the ship docked and asked to see the Captain. I saw him, but it was a civilian with him who did all the talking. It turned out he was known as the Commodore and was in charge of the handing-over trials. He read the riot act and finished up by saying: "We are going to fire a missile on Monday and if it doesn't work we shall put your system over the side!" A charming man!

The small party then went to inspect the launcher. Armour noted at once that the transmitter was mounted "solid as a rock" and must have absorbed violent vibration when the missile was fired. He knew it had to come off the launcher. So he chose a spot for the transmitter adjacent to the other electronics below deck. Having no spares, he managed to make the new connections with scraps of surplus cabling left over from the original installation. Working right through without a break until early Monday morning, he still had no way of knowing whether the guidance signal was now transmitting through the aerial, which was still on the launcher.

The frigate sailed at eight o'clock and a radio-controlled target had been laid on for 2 pm. A short time before, the *Seacat* crew took up their positions –

Suddenly everyone started pointing and there was the target coming in at low altitude. The missile took off and it was immediately clear to us that it was under control. It swung round in the direction of the target, steadied and, after what appeared to be an interminable wait, the target disintegrated in a ball of flame. The cheers were deafening. We just collapsed.

We were invited to the Captain's quarters for dinner where the Commodore was presiding. He was a different man. After having lived on galley scraps for two days we enjoyed a beautiful dinner and especially the wine. I set off for London and arrived at the Knightsbridge flat around midnight. I fell into bed, the first one I had seen since early Friday morning.[7]

Jackson's related problem with *Tigercat* was settled overnight: by mounting the transmitter on big rubber pads to kill the vibration. 100 per cent. successful firings of *Tigercat* were achieved the following day. Later in 1969 the Commander-in-Chief of the Imperial Iranian Air Force, General Khatami, and ten other generals, witnessed a repeat performance. Export sales resumed their buoyant course.

The transmitter problem also hit the *Tigercats* shipped out to Jordan, but fortunately before their first firing. This kingdom, delicately sandwiched between Israel and Iraq and land-locked apart from a sole outlet into the Red Sea at the Gulf of Aqaba, had its own political troubles. At one stage at this time the Palestine Liberation Organisation held Short's team of training engineers hostage in their hotel in Amman. As Jackson recalled –

Trouble was brewing with the PLO. Bill Allen, Head of Weapons Application Department and Jack McFarlane, Commercial Manager, had gone to the airport, leaving Red Reilly, Weapons Application Engineer, to clear up some business details, when the terrorists decided to take over the hotel, holding all foreigners prisoner. Apparently some of the younger Brits started to get stroppy, but Red, with his much wiser old head, took charge and cooled the situation down; but it lasted a few days.

The first firing of *Tigercat* was attended by King Hussein and was pretty spectacular. As the target, a Northrop KD2R5 unmanned drone approached, it was engaged by anti-aircraft fire without success. Then *Tigercat* was fired, knocking it out in a ball of flame. The King was most impressed and invited Allen and his team to lunch. Bill refused as the team had no change of clothes. But an ADC returned to say the King wasn't changing either. It was as a result of that day that the King presented medals to the team and an order to Bill Allen.[8]

The Order of Istiqlal was awarded by King Hussein of Jordan to (from left) Ian Richardson, Jimmy McClelland, Billy Walker, Harry Thomas BEM, Captain Bill Allen, Sam Young and Red Reilly for their assistance in establishing Tigercat in service.

Hussein II, Harrow and Sandhurst-educated, was a sympathetic friend; but he had another shared interest. He was a keen radio "ham". Communication with the Jordan team was simplified and improved because its leader was also an enthusiastic "ham" who spoke to a colleague in Castlereagh regularly. Sharing the royal interest did the team no harm.

Refinement of the missile was a continuing process. One example was the radio-controlled miniature FM altimeter fitted to *Seacat*. Because it was fitted into one of the wings, the design of the missile did not have to be modified. This was a latterday spin-off from Hugh Conway's famous suggestion at a bull session years before that the missile needed a ball and chain to keep it on course at low altitudes in its surface-to-surface mode. Flying low, against a sea-skimming radar-evading aircraft, *Seacat* could ditch in the water. The altimeter provided the answer.[9] This capability also allowed *Seacat* to be used as a target simulating sea-skimming missiles.

The missile would be in service for many years to come but the scope for improvement and uprating was limited. The Castlereagh team knew that *Seacat* and its derivative, *Tigercat,* were ageing rapidly. The way ahead pointed towards an entirely new weapon.

Seacat fitted with the height cushion provided a sea skimming target for naval practice

NOTES

1   Anthony Sampson: The Arms Bazaar (London, 1977), p296

2   Sampson, op.cit., pp297–8

3   Cf. also Chapter 13

4   Jackson, interview with author

5   Do.

6   Do.

7   Armour, op.cit., pp 151-2

8   Jackson, interview with author

9   Cf. Chapter 8

12

BLOWPIPE

THE research team at Castlereagh turned its mind to the challenge of finding a successor to *Seacat* immediately the ship-borne missile had gone into production. There was general agreement that they should stay with short-range weapons. They had the field to themselves and the bigger fish in the business nationally were well dug into high-altitude weaponry; although, in marked contrast to Castlereagh, they had had little success in export sales. But the consensus was that a new weapon would have to deal with the same brand of airborne target, coming in beneath the radar cover, but possibly coming in a great deal faster. Martin Armour has explained how the new weapon was born over a quiet drink with a colleague in a country pub beyond the northern fringes of Belfast one Friday evening –

> I had no car at that time and every Friday night he used to drive me home. On the way we invariably stopped at Corr's pub, which at that time was a small bar, part of a small house. There was an alcove in the bar with a round marble-topped table and we always sat there. It was there that the subject of the new missile came up….He said that the aimer's task in guiding *Seacat* was really quite difficult, as the aimer had to move the joystick by varying amounts to get the required manoeuvres. He thought that what was known as a 'bang-bang' system would be easier. With this system, any movement of the joystick would result in the wings going to their limits and staying there until the aimer returned the joystick to its central position. Also he said we could get away with much smaller wings and a much smaller control unit, possibly one powered by electric motors rather than the complicated hydraulic system.[1]

Armour admitted he was fascinated and told his colleague to go ahead and knock up a model of the control unit. A few weeks later it was ready. He was amazed to see it was a mere three inches in diameter and only nine inches long. Another colleague seized upon it at once, exclaiming that he could design a shoulder-launched missile with a control unit the same size. In fact *Blowpipe* eventually emerged with a length of three and a half feet because that was the length of his design engineer's drawing board.

Early test firings of *Blowpipe* were carried out on the Company estate near Helen's Bay in Co Down. Note the celebratory bottle on the mantlepiece.

Soon a project team was working on the new weapon. They called it *Blowpipe*. The chosen label, identified with the lethal bamboo tube used by South American Indians to shoot darts tipped with the paralysing poison, curare, conveyed a suitable message of menace. *Blowpipe* was very new; but, wisely, it incorporated the winning qualities of Seacat: simplicity, cheapness and instant readiness. The binoculars to track the target and the thumb-operated joystick, transmitting its guidance signals through a radio command link, had been kept. The breakthrough lay in its lightweight and compact size. It could be switched to action mode in just twenty seconds.

The science of electronics was growing up. Transistors having replaced the bulky and vulnerable old glass valves of *Seacat* Mod 0, the result was that seven *Blowpipes* were to weigh less than one *Seacat*. Moreover, at 24lb. and with a diameter of only three and a half inches, it could be carried by one soldier, launched from his shoulder and even dropped by parachute in a purpose-built pack containing several rounds. A telescopic leg allowed the operator to keep the weapon in readiness mode for long periods.

But the aimer's proximity to the actual firing raised new problems. Blowpipe was contained in its own slim canister. This was managed by folding back the tips of the tail so that the tail unit, essential to control the flight, would fit inside. At the back end of the canister was a panel which kept the missile secure before use but when the aimer pressed the firing button, the panel blew off with such velocity that troops standing behind would be in danger. The hazard was removed by fitting a miniature parachute to the panel made from strands of linen tape with a small plastic diaphragm at the end. This introduced enough

Missiles with first stage motors were fired into straw bales, the results being monitored by Bob McIvor.

drag to slow down the ejection of the panel. But when testing was carried out on the Army's Larkhill firing range on Salisbury Plain, several missiles in succession ended up nose-diving into the ground. One film sequence captured a missile out of control hurtling towards the camera because the woman in charge of it bravely kept her finger on the button until the projectile thudded into the ground a few feet in front of her.

George Townend and his team found it difficult to resist despair. But the fault had to be located. Its nature is a nice illustration of the supreme level of precision essential in this branch of miniaturised engineering. After much checking they found the cause in the little piece of narrow tubing, a venturi, fitted to the canister behind the tail. Its function was to accelerate the expulsion of the expanding gases released on firing. The designers had left one 30,000th of an inch inside the tubing to take the resin required to bond it in position. But as the resin set, the weight of the component dropped it down that 30,000th of an inch and the gases were being expelled from the venturi at an angle which was driving the missile down. "We simply fixed it by lifting it up," said Townend. "That solved our problem; but they were anxious moments."

Blowpipe made its first public appearance at the Farnborough Air Show of 1966. It was a delicate moment. *Blowpipe* was still Shorts' own project, devoid of outside support. Government had evinced little interest. But within the Army there were tacticians who were very aware of the enhanced threat to ground forces from hedge-skimming fighters carrying missiles and cluster bombs. They had gone to an airfield to inspect the RAF Regiment's *Tigercat* defences, but decided they were not mobile enough. The American *Redeye*, later the *Stinger*, was selling well and was another option; but, being a heat-seeker, it was limited to chasing the target's exhaust after it had gone by, a penalty in combating attacking aircraft head-on, and it could then be countered by the target aircraft releasing flares. *Blowpipe*, of course, had not this limitation; but Armour took a *Blowpipe* on a sales tour to Canada; then to Germany, Italy and Greece, all with no result. At home though, Army interest increased and the sales drive was renewed.[2]

The following year the new weapon was promoted from an in-house enterprise (as it had begun) to the status of Government-aided project RF268. Further development was now to be Government-funded, the result of an appraisal by the new Ministry of Technology which had conceded that there were good prospects for export sales.

After some fifty experimental launches to ensure that the safety devices were failsafe, the first crucial firings from the shoulder were made by Jack McBride, Assistant Head of the Technical Department, who was responsible for designing the two-stage motor in conjunction with RPE Westcott. It was in the grounds of Rathmoyle

The first shoulder firing of *Blowpipe* by Jack McBride in 1968.

House, Shorts' guest residence at Helen's Bay in County Down, on 12 September 1968. On the eve of the Farnborough show and before an audience of Army brass, McBride became the first person in the United Kingdom to fire a guided missile from the shoulder.

At the show itself a week later, Vickers of Barrow, the armaments and shipbuilding group, was to announce a private venture involving the design of a multiple launcher for *Blowpipe* for use on submarine decks and surface craft. This eventually went as far as successful trials though it never went into production. But the venture increased defence interest in the new weapon and was another step towards acceptance. Soon afterwards the Royal Artillery embarked upon a gruelling test programme for the missile, including one hundred firings, some with live warheads against target aircraft, and involving the roughest usage to simulate battle conditions and air drops in combat. The result was a substantial production order from the Army in 1973.

Installation of the *Blowpipe* Submarine Launched Air Missile (SLAM) on board a Vickers Submarine

Seacat sales over its long life involved supplying the navies of 16 nations. *Tigercat* sold to the armed forces of six countries, the exports alone being worth some £30m. *Blowpipe*, boosted by the Army order, was later to sell to twenty armed forces abroad in a dozen different countries. But its introduction involved new requirements. Rough handling on the battlefield was one. The environmental test department at Castlereagh did its best to simulate the worst

The radio-controlled *Blowpipe* during practice firings by The Royal Thai Airforce

conditions. Blowpipe in its robust foam-filled fibreglass field pack was designed to withstand a fall from the back of an Army lorry, a drop of about four and a half feet, even though it contained delicate electronic and electro-mechanical devices, not to mention a warhead. A special additional pack was fitted for parachute drops and storage. Climatic extremes, from the tropics to the Arctic, also had to be accommodated.

Blowpipe being para-dropped during exercises on
Slemish mountain, County Antrim in 1972

The success of *Blowpipe* involved a major innovation at Castlereagh. It was to be the first missile which Shorts assembled into its finished state using only the facilities of its own guided weapons division. *Seacat*, notably, had left the factory as a kit. Important components, such as the motor, were fitted during final assembly by the navy concerned. Above all, the warhead had to be fitted in a specialised plant equipped for handling munitions. This was the real reason for the kit. Shorts, in the early days of Castlereagh, had no facility to handle explosives. But *Seacat's* success, and the knowledge that there was going to be a missile family, convinced the company that this liability must be removed.

It was not a propitious moment to attempt it. Northern Ireland was in a volatile state. The 25 people who died in 1970, in the political disturbances which accompanied the dying years of the old Stormont regime, became 174 the year after and 470 in the worst year, 1972. During those twelve months nearly 5,000 other people suffered wounds in explosions or shootings. In fact there was one school of thought in the Whitehall service departments which favoured moving missile manufacture out of Northern Ireland altogether. It was a fact that, from the beginning, officials at the Ministry of Defence had been uneasy about guided weapons being assembled in Northern Ireland at all. A policy decision against its continuance was something which could never be excluded, bearing in mind that Shorts was still Government-owned.

But it would have been strongly resisted by the employees, who possessed an expertise which could not readily be replicated; and the company, for which Castlereagh was a valuable and consistent profit-maker, would have been anxious lest a move would lead to a hiving off or even absorption by competitors. These had long cast a jealous eye upon Castlereagh's record of technological innovation and upon an export success which they had never been able to match. In fact vacant facilities to accommodate the Castlereagh production had even been earmarked at a possible new site at Leyland in Lancashire.[3]

The fact that the Army was unwilling to do what the Navy had done in setting up its own assembly units for *Seacat* meant that the need for a site where explosives could be handled safely was urgent. But many of the Castlereagh team were pessimistic about the prospects. The disturbed public atmosphere in the community at large outside the plant was the main reason. But John Potts, Assistant Chief Engineer of the Division, was determined to prove them wrong –

> We had these Monday morning meetings - ten people round a table. Nine thought we could never do the explosives thing because of the security threat and we'd never get an explosives plant because of the situation on the streets. But I volunteered to try to get it. I knew there were unused facilities in England some of the Ministry of Defence people had in mind and some of them wouldn't even come to Belfast for meetings because they couldn't get additional personal insurance. But I said I'd look into it.[4]

Potts was another Yorkshireman, attracted to Belfast in 1958 from the wind tunnel department of A. V. Roe by John Dent, then Chief Engineer. Potts' last duty before leaving Shorts to become Industrial Liaison Officer at Queen's University in Belfast was effectively to save the Castlereagh missile plant for Northern Ireland.

Having telephoned Stormont after that Monday meeting, Potts went up to see the Minister of Home Affairs, the then Robert Porter, later in the same week. He found the civil servants present opposed to the idea of a new explosives plant. But he pressed his case strongly, pointing out that obtaining the new facility was the only way to keep the valuable missile industry in Northern Ireland. The meeting ended with hand-shaking all round and a promise from the Minister to do all he could to help.

Shortly afterwards Potts was provided with the data he had sought: the list of all the establishments in Northern Ireland which in the past had been licensed and equipped to handle explosives; and he felt the battle might be on the way to being won. In fact there was quite a choice: one in Londonderry, another in Carrickfergus and a third at Kinnegar in Holywood. This last was attractive, it was so near, but the licence would only provide enough explosives to supply two days' production of missiles a week. Then he fastened upon Killough Harbour on the shores of County Down near the fishing port of Ardglass: it was licensed to import up to two thousand tons of high explosive in one shipment. Barely twelve miles away was an old property of the Ministry of Defence. It had been used by the Navy to test torpedoes during the Second World War and had a similar licence.

Potts knew about the old explosives depot in the countryside beyond the village of Crossgar in County Down. It was used as an ammunition dump during the First World War. It already had secure fencing and security lighting. It was well off the main roads; yet it was also within twenty miles of Castlereagh. But the Ministry of Defence, in one of the periodic economy drives which afflict Government, had recently issued instructions that it was to be sold. Recognising that the site would provide an answer to Shorts' problem on explosives handling, Potts got in touch with the Ministry of Defence land agent in Northern Ireland, Leslie Ayris, and explained the delicacy of the situation. Ayris proving sympathetic, the pair determined to connive between them to frustrate the sale. But managerial colleagues at Shorts warned him he was going out on a limb and doing something for which he had no authority —

I got no support for my actions. . and indeed my boss warned me I was over-extended and perhaps would be in trouble. I even arranged for the long grass to be cut and the roads and areas around the forty-two buildings to be cleaned up and estimates of conversion prepared when we had no legal right of access. But events proved me right. Long after I left, attending a Shorts retirement party, I was introduced: "You'd better meet John Potts. No John Potts, no Crossgar." My thanks were in seeing the missile business kept in Northern Ireland despite the troubles, when there was a great risk of its being moved to vacant facilities in England.[5]

In fact the isolated situation of the site minimised the security problem. There was only one house within a mile. The company was later to take it over, giving the farmer who lived there right of access and extending the perimeter fence to include it. But it was natural, given the highly volatile political climate in Northern Ireland in the early 1970s, that the security men from the Ministry of Defence would be exacting. Armour records that, once the new use of the site was officially agreed, the inspectors arrived in force –

> They knew, just as we did, that there were some areas not many miles away where the Union flag did not fly. However they only uncovered one security problem. This was that the floodlights round the perimeter fence took several minutes to get to full illuminance. This was no problem as long as the mains supply was in operation. But if we had a mains power failure and had to bring on the emergency generator, there could have been a period of three or four minutes before full visibility was restored. The lights were replaced by instant security lights.[6]

Sensitive problems remained, of course. There was the matter of the delivery of warheads to the new facility and of the missiles, completely fabricated, leaving the plant. But Army goodwill was enlisted by airlifting a party of senior officers for an inspection tour, followed by lunch built around the superintendent's wife's Irish stew. Soon the vital new site was launched, with the missiles arriving from Castlereagh to await fitting of warhead and motor and with a modest staff of about thirty. But they worked behind a formidable security screen. This consisted of double perimeter fences with a dead zone between patrolled by guards with dogs.

The explosives still had to be conveyed to Crossgar, a delicate operation at the best of times: and of course it was far from being the best of times in Northern Ireland. The task fell to Shorts' Chief Test Pilot, Lindsay Cumming, to ferry the cargo once a week from Glasgow Airport at Abbotsinch. The explosives would arrive there in a green box lorry with police escort. Cumming, accompanied by a policeman from Crossgar, would have his Short *Skyvan* (later an SD330) stationed on the far side of the airfield from the passenger terminal. There, away from the public gaze, the 18 boxes from the ICI explosives factory nearby, each weighing 80lb, would be loaded for the one-hour flight. As he explained –

> We all called it the Schweppes run. I never saw inside a box. Everything was on a need-to-know basis; and of course the boxes never went near Castlereagh and they weren't allowed to land at Sydenham. We had to

land at Aldergrove and park down at the old Maintenance Unit site, looking half right from the front of the passenger terminal. The RAF helicoptered the stuff from Aldergrove into Crossgar. There was consideration of building an airstrip we could fly into direct. But it never happened.[7]

Cumming ran a similar shuttle to and from the airport at Samlesbury, near Preston, to collect the motors for the missiles from the former English Electric plant, later part of British Aerospace.

Crossgar as it is known in Castlereagh, was a sprawling site of 109.45 acres, complete with its own network of internal roads, surrounded by barbed wire. Among the extensive buildings were two semi-detached houses. One was immediately allocated to a security man and he was the first Shorts staff to take up his post. Even now, though, Castlereagh does not own the Crossgar plant, for the Government, in law, was unable to sell it to the company. They were bound to give the dozen or so local farmers from which the land had been compulsorily purchased first refusal if there was to be a disposal. So, the property having been transferred from Defence, Castlereagh became a tenant paying rent to the new Ministry of Technology.

Blowpipe even had its sensitive moments before its explosives were fitted. During its development phase, missiles for test firings at the Army's Larkhill range in Wiltshire were taken regularly on the then BEA scheduled flights from Aldergrove airport by Castlereagh staff. Being without warheads, the free space was filled with test gear. As George Jackson explained –

> The security people at Aldergrove knew all about it; so there was no problem, except that we used to carry the boxes into the aeroplane and keep them on our laps. Nobody ever said anything. I was going over for a demonstration firing for the Danes and I went through security, having my bag checked and everything; and then this box. The woman said suddenly in a loud voice: "That's a *Blowpipe* missile, isn't it?" I looked askance. "I used to work down at the GW factory, Queen's Island," she said."[8]

Testing *Blowpipe* had raised new problems. Normally in a case like this the manufacturer will use the space, later to be filled in the armed missile by its warhead and fuse, to fit in the telemetry gear which feeds back data by radio link on the test flight. This can then be married with the film record showing the behaviour in the air. But *Blowpipe's* diameter of a mere three inches (less than half of *Seacat's*) meant that there was scant room for telemetry. The Royal Aircraft Establishment at Farnborough came to the rescue with a temporary solution, a scratch recorder, an instrument which scratched a performance track on coated celluloid. This could be squeezed in; but it was then essential to recover the missile and the recorder in it. The cameras gave the impact zone, but locating the small hole the missile made in the chalky soil was the problem. Various bright ideas were tried including scenting the missile from a bitch on heat and using tracker dogs! The solution adopted was to fix a modified shotgun cartridge at the rear of the missile which fired aluminium foil on impact. The development of a telemetry sender to suit Blowpipe not only relieved the problem but, by providing feedback by radio, greatly enhanced the information from each firing.

Meantime, while the salesmen were busy negotiating deals of steadily increasing value during the second half of the 1970s, the designers' heads were down in the continuous quest to refine the product – and in the 1980s, Seacat, Tigercat and Blowpipe were to go to war.

NOTES

1   Armour, op.cit, p 154

2   Do. p156

3   John Potts, interview with author

4   Do.

5   Do.

6   Armour, op.cit, p158

7   Lindsay Cumming, interview with author

8   Jackson, interview with author

13

INTO BATTLE

THE invasion of the Falkland Islands by 800 Argentinian marines at 4.30 am on 2 April 1982 is remembered in the popular mind as having come out of the blue. In reality, it did not. The rank and file of officialdom, it is true, were flabbergasted. When a BBC radio producer rang the Foreign Office in the small hours to check a rumour, the duty officer dismissed it, remarking that if anything were happening they would know. In fact, things were about to happen on East Falkland. An invasion fleet was sailing towards the islands – but, due to a failure of communications with the South Atlantic, the Foreign and Commonwealth Office knew nothing.[1]

Those at the top, though, were well aware of the risk, even if it suited ministers, belatedly stung to action, that the fable of total surprise should be allowed to take hold. In fact, although the Foreign Secretary, Lord Carrington, felt obliged to resign on 5 April because his department appeared to have been taken unawares, British naval forces were already being diverted to the South Atlantic even before the Argentinians landed at Mullett Creek, south of Port Stanley.[2] But however the invasion was presented, Margaret Thatcher knew she was negotiating the knife-edge of crisis. As she cobbled together the task force on an expeditionary scale not seen in Britain since Suez, all potential excuses were harboured gratefully against the real risk of disaster. She was later praised, quite legitimately, for her resolution; but it would have availed nothing had she not been blest with the essential attribute of all successful military adventurers – a remarkable run of good luck.

In fact early warnings of the Argentinians' suspected intention had been flagged through intelligence and diplomatic channels, American as well as British, weeks in advance. The invasion bid had a most venerable origin. The islands had had a turbulent colonial history involving France, Spain and Great Britain. The new United Provinces of Rio de la Plata – precursor of Argentina – sent a frigate to claim them in 1820. Amid constant disputes over trading and fishing rights, two British warships hove to off the islands in 1833 and reasserted British sovereignty, first declared in 1765. British administration

Map of the Falklands Islands

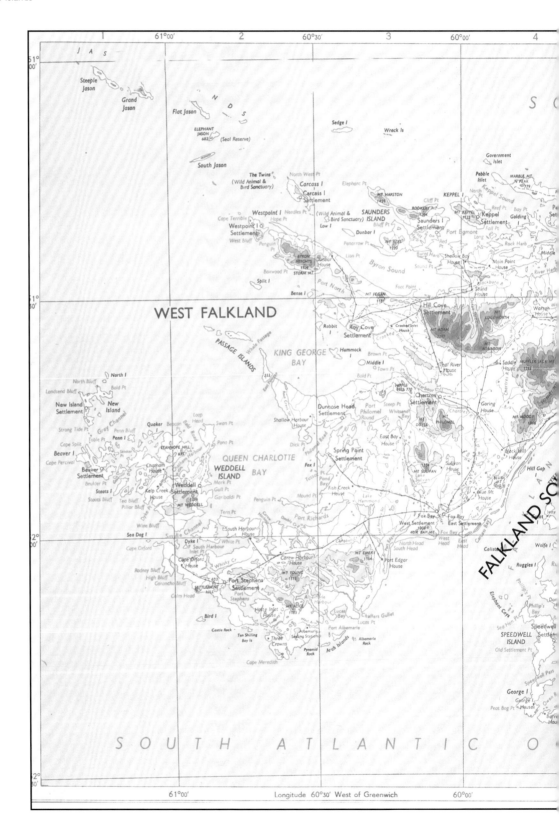

continued, but has never been acquiesced in by Argentina.

It was the traditional task of the Royal Navy to protect them; but this was a responsibility which continued to grow in difficulty as, one by one, the old imperial outposts were surrendered. The humiliation of Suez in 1956 accelerated the flight. The symbolism was clear and the Navy shrank in concert. Swingeing defence cuts followed as the nation sought to adjust to its lesser international role.

There was less money voted for armaments, making it all the more remarkable that *Seacat* sold so well in this chilly political and financial climate. The secret was its sheer cost-effectiveness as a weapon. By the late 1970s, however, fifteen years after the missile entered service with the Navy, constant cutting back was taking its toll. Many British warships were in difficulty over lack of spare parts. Their sailors were so poorly paid that many of those in shore bases had second jobs. In 1980 there was a total embargo on new defence contracts. A year later the Treasury imposed a further brutal review of costs on the Defence Secretary, John Nott, leading to the resignation of his Navy Minister, Keith Speed, a former Lieutenant-Commander in the Reserve.[3]

It was on this tenuous basis that the Navy contemplated involving almost 30,000 British servicemen and hazarding a battle fleet, 8,000 miles from their source of supply, against the rival surface and air forces of a proud South American nation. The Argentinians would be operating close to their home bases and their forces, like the British, would be equipped with many of the preferred weapons available in Europe and America—including Shorts' missiles. The Argentinians had *Seacat*, *Tigercat* and *Blowpipe*; the British were using *Seacat* and *Blowpipe*; both also relied upon the big Boeing *Chinook* helicopters and Lockheed C130 *Hercules* transports and Argentina used two Short *Skyvans* for transport to and from the mainland. One of these, standing on Stanley Racecourse, was damaged by British naval gunfire during early raids by SAS and SBS patrols on the night of 3 and 4 of May. Immobilised, it was finally destroyed by British artillery during the night of 12 and 13 June, just before the ceasefire. Overlaps in training made this an even more extraordinary war, with Argentinian officers having been accustomed to regular visits to British Army training depots.

When the invasion fleet was known to have sailed, one of the most urgent counter-measures to be mounted on the British side was a programme to jam the guidance systems of the Shorts missiles with which the Argentinians were equipped. A priority call from Whitehall came into Shorts to assemble their top weapons technicians at once at Castlereagh. *Blowpipe's* guidance system could operate on many different wavelengths. "They wanted us to devise a jamming signal," said Sir Philip Foreman, "which would incapacitate them. We had to work in shifts round the clock. I think they also changed the frequency of the *Seacats* being used by the Royal Navy so they couldn't be jammed by the Argentinians, who had identical equipment."[4]

The engineers devised a matchbox-sized unit containing a transmitter whose frequency would upset the enemy's *Blowpipe* guidance system. First, though, it was essential to be certain the oncoming aircraft was the enemy. Accordingly the unit's signal, using its IFF setting (Identification – Friend or Foe), gave the aimer sitting at his missile launcher an instant feedback. Once enemy status was confirmed, the disabling function could be brought into play.

Maurice McFadden explained how he and his colleagues felt in the knowledge that armaments they had developed and made might now quite possibly be turned on their own kith and kin –

> On the news we saw the Argentinians unloading *Seacat* on to the harbour at Port Stanley. It was highly embarrassing. We had to work overtime to perfect the countermeasures. *Seacat*, you see, was just like model aircraft with the model builders using different radio channels to control them from the ground. The idea was that you could have two or three users all firing *Seacats* and one wouldn't interfere with the other.

> But in the case of the countermeasures, we had to transmit a signal that would affect them all. We all knew what channels they were using and we did it. In effect it meant having a transmitter directed at the firing point - about two or three miles range.[5]

The guided weapons employed by both sides in some cases had been around for many years; there had been ample time – and good reason – to anticipate the problems joint ownership in a war would produce. *Seacat* and *Tigercat* were Britain's most widely exported missiles. *Seacat* had been in service with the Royal Navy for twenty years, *Tigercat* with the RAF for fifteen. Even the newest, *Blowpipe*, was the product of development during the mid-1960s and had been part of the Army's weaponry since 1975. But it had been a long international peace and budget cuts discouraged commitment of funds to contingency planning.

In the event the Argentinian invasion force arrived with their Shorts' missiles ready for operation. Immediately after their landing and the capitulation of the Falklands garrison of some sixty Royal Marines, supported by the twenty-three Territorials who could be mustered around Stanley, they moved quickly to fortify the air strip. They had few aircraft with them, so guns and missiles were of prime importance. The troops had *Blowpipe* detachments in every garrison and they set up three *Tigercat* fire units between the airport and the town.[6]

But what each side still lacked was the opportunity for battle testing. However rigorous and relentless the trials, there could be no substitute for the unique stress of the battlefield. The most important lesson each side learned on and around the Falklands was what its missiles could do and what they could not.

For the British the chief offensive fear from the other side was the surface-to-surface French *Exocet* because the Navy had no effective long-range counter to its sea-skimming ability. Yet even the *Exocet*, around which a kind of mythology grew immediately after the war, was not new: it dated from 1971. The mythology derived from the fact that the Falklands was the first theatre where it was spectacularly deployed. Jack Higgins' thriller of 1983 revived its aura of menace.[7] Again, both sides had it. Sixteen feet nine inches long and with a diameter of one foot three inches, it carried an explosive charge of 363 lb. over 45 miles (70 kms.) at a speed of Mach 1, about 680 mph; many of the Navy's frigates in the task force were equipped with it.

As things stood before battle had been joined, Rear-Admiral John Woodward's tactical plan was to keep his aircraft carriers out of range. If the Argentinians put to sea, he would withdraw eastwards at high speed, hoping they would follow until they reached the limit of their fuel range. Two attack groups would then close in to engage them. The first consisted of three Type 42 destroyers; the second had the larger destroyer, *Glamorgan* with two Type 21 frigates. The Glamorgan carried two quad *Seacat* launchers and the frigates each had one. But the Type 42 destroyers in the first attack group did not. Instead they had *Sea Dart* (so had the Argentinians): like many missiles of its age it had been designed primarily to hit high-flying Russian aircraft and could not engage sea-skimming targets. This lesson was to be rammed home brutally when the *Sheffield*, a Type 42, was to be hit by an *Exocet* at 10am on 20 April, 40 miles south of Port Stanley.

Identification of incoming targets was to prove a recurrent problem for the task force on both land and sea. When the first blip on the *Sheffield's* radar indicated an unknown aircraft, there was speculation that it might be a returning *Harrier* or an enemy plane on a bombing run. Two and a half minutes later, officers on the bridge, chillingly, saw the missile skimming above the waves towards them. Five seconds later it struck amidships, eight feet above the waterline. Efforts to put out the resultant fires were unavailing. Forty casualties were taken off and the order given to the remainder of the 268 crew to abandon ship. But twenty-one of them were dead. Four days later, while under tow, *Sheffield* turned over and sank.[8] Her loss underlined afresh the irrationality of the war. Two sister ships of *Sheffield*, guided missile destroyers, were built for Argentina; and when the *Sheffield* suffered fire damage in the stern during construction in the 1970s, a matching stern section taken from the *Hercules*, being built for Argentina, was fitted as a replacement to ensure her delivery on time.[9]

This first dramatisation of the power of the modern missile was a chastening experience for the task force. The apparent ease and the precise accuracy of the single-shot direct hit appalled the nucleus of

Second World War sailors serving in it. The absence of effective counter-measures shocked them. The Argentinians were known to have had five *Exocets*, but to be negotiating to obtain more from the weapon's French fabricators, Aerospatiale. They were to fail; but for long uncertainty reigned. Would they obtain the missiles from a third party? The British did not know. As a propaganda weapon, the power of the *Exocet* AM39 was supreme.

The silent and prowling nuclear submarine was another new element. The very opportunities to employ the Argentinians' *Seacat* launchers in the later stages of the war were to be limited because, after the sinking of their light cruiser, *General Belgrano*, they never brought warships within striking range of the task force again. The 13,645-ton *Belgrano* had been built by the Americans as the light cruiser, *Boise*. They had too many of them after 1945 and six were sold to South American navies. Argentina got the *Boise* in 1951 and renamed it *Diecisiete de Octobre*. Later it was again renamed and in the 1970s fitted with Dutch radar and two quad *Seacat* launchers.[10] But they were never fired in anger during the Falklands war. Notoriously, the *General Belgrano* (as the *Boise* had now become), with a crew of more than a thousand on board, was well outside, and steaming away from, the total exclusion zone when she was sunk. The Royal Navy nuclear submarine, Conqueror, scored two hits, on the port bow and in the stern, with a series of conventional torpedoes on the afternoon of 2 May.

The first sustained air engagements of the war were to take place three weeks later on 21 May, when the task force moved in to establish beachheads at San Carlos Water. Here the missile systems were put to their first serious test. The *Rapier* surface-to-air missiles, which were being heavily relied upon to protect the newly-disembarked force, ran into serious trouble with their batteries. Long exposure to salt at sea on the voyage south played havoc with their electronics and access to spare parts was difficult. It had been almost a year since the operators had practised live firing and it showed up in their tracking.[11]

Sea Wolf, the short-range low-level ship-to-air weapon, was handicapped because its tracking radar was upset by the clutter of military vehicles and equipment on the ground inshore. Its computer was also confused when several aircraft approached at once.[12] The Navy felt they were going to have to rely heavily on the visually tracked missiles like *Seacat* and *Blowpipe*.

During the British landing at San Carlos on 21 May, the frigate, *Argonaut*, suffered damage and casualties from a low-level Aeromacchi. While a *Wessex* helicopter was preparing to winch off casualties, *Skyhawks* appeared. It was a perfect test for a quick-reaction missile system. While the helicopter made for the shore, *Argonaut* released a *Seacat*, bringing one of the *Skyhawks* down in the harbour. But a bomb entered the boiler room. Another lodged in her *Seacat* magazine aft, resting on live missile rounds. The bomb did not explode but several missiles did. The vessel lost power, but lines were quickly rigged to the forward *Seacat* launcher to connect it to the ship's diesel generator, keeping the missile system operational.[13]

Blowpipe aimers were to have their own difficulties, particularly in tracking targets crossing their line of sight or receding as opposed to those approaching. Over-eagerness may have played a part: as Max Hastings, the *Evening Standard* war correspondent who landed with the Commandos at San Carlos, noted, "They fired their rifles and machine guns and *Blowpipes* whenever an attacker came within miles, to the dismay of the logistics staff, desperate to husband ammunition —"[14]

Then there were the evasive tactics adopted by the Argentinian pilots which proved difficult for the missile aimers to neutralise. The airmen flew at less than a hundred feet, making expert use of the undulations and low hills for concealment until the last moment before pressing home the attack. The Argentinians, though, lost nineteen planes in the course of their sorties opposing the San Carlos landing between 21 and 25 May.[15] On 22nd, a pair of *Skyhawks*, flying low, made a bombing run on the Type 21 frigate, *Antelope*. Her cannon fire succeeded in turning them away. But the vessel's *Seacat* aimer lined up on one Skyhawk, the missile overtaking it and bringing it down.[16]

The assault ship, *Fearless*, completed by Harland & Wolff at the end of 1965, was equipped with four quad *Seacat* launchers. On 24 May, having put her four landing craft ashore, she was standing off San Carlos and brought down two more Argentinian aircraft with *Seacat* rounds.

The deterrent effect of *Seacat* and *Blowpipe* fire must be added to the number of its kills. In this the unique circumstances of the Falklands conflict played an important part. The Argentinian pilots faced a total journey out and back of 900 miles or more, depending upon which mainland base they were using, leaving them with fuel for only a single sortie over the target. *Seacat* had a large warhead of formidable appearance in flight. In some cases it was off-putting enough when fired for a pilot to abort his mission.[18] But inexperience led to mistakes, as George Townend recalled —

> The Army put Blowpipe on top of the hills. The Argie planes were coming along in the valleys beneath the radar. The missile aimers hadn't a hope because they were against the skyline, silhouetted. So it was a bad strategy.[19]

But campaign experience generally was paying off. Once the ground forces were dug in on beachheads after landing at San Carlos Water on 21 May, a three-pronged assault towards Stanley began.

One arm of this involved a lunge twenty miles southwards towards Goose Green by 2nd battalion, Parachute Regiment on 28 May. With them they had two *Blowpipe* detachments: the first, from the Guided Weapons Regiment, Royal Artillery, had been with them since the landing. Carrying the bulky field packs, they had had difficulty in keeping up with the Paras. So now Lt. Col. H. Jones, the commanding officer of 2nd Para, asked for a Royal Marine *Blowpipe* detachment because he knew they would be super fit for the rest of the trek.[20]

It was in an attempt to take Darwin hill just under two miles north of Goose Green that Jones was mortally wounded in the neck. Shortly afterwards, in atrocious weather with low cloud, the Paras came under attack from *Pucaras*. These twin-engined turo-prop ground attack aircraft carried a vicious armament of machine guns and cannon. They also had rocket pods under the wings and napalm canisters on fuselage racks and were dreaded for their ability to slow-manoeuvre and take out helicopters. Dropping napalm and firing rockets, they now downed one of two *Scout* helicopters which had been bringing up ammunition and ferrying back wounded, and which had been summoned to rescue Jones. The second *Scout* only made its escape because of the ferocity of the *Blowpipe* and machine gun fire from the ground. Marine Strange of 3rd Commando Brigade Air Defence Troop stood up "as though in a butt at a grouse drive" and shot down one Aeromacchi at 2km range with his *Blowpipe*. It crashed near the perimeter of the Goose Green airfield, killing its pilot and drenching the Paras and Commandos with fuel from its ruptured tanks. Miraculously, the fuel did not ignite. In addition a *Pucara* was taken out by concentrated rifle fire.[21] In fact as early as 21st May Argentinian air operations had been severely restricted at Goose Green. After enduring the *Blowpipe* barrage, the Argentinians were slow to hazard their *Pucaras* in a leading role again.

But naval commanders on the spot were to argue that the switch from guns to missiles had been too fast: scepticism doubtless inspired by the truism that missile launchers could not be instantly everywhere. The low-level bombing raid at Fitzroy Settlement, twenty miles south-west of Stanley, by two *Skyhawks* and two *Mirages* on the early afternoon of 8 June, brutally rammed the lesson home. In the process the landing ship, *Sir Galahad*, unloading men and stores in the bay without anti-aircraft cover, was turned into a flaming cauldron. The raid cost fifty-one lives, including thirty-three Welsh Guardsmen. In hindsight it could have been avoided. *Rapier* missiles, asked for, could not be provided in time. *Blowpipes*, much more quickly activated, might have been organised from the one thousand troops already ashore, but were not. Amazingly, there was no ship-to-shore communication.

The frigate, *Plymouth*, was attacked by five *Mirages* in Falkland Sound almost simultaneously with the disaster befalling the *Galahad*. Her *Seacat* caught the first Mirage and a gunner the second, but the vessel sustained four direct hits with heavy bombs.[22]

As always in modern warfare, mastery of the air was the decisive issue. On land the Argentinians shot down one *Harrier* and two helicopters with *Blowpipe*. But the task force succeeded in so mauling the Argentinian air arm that after 26 May the Brititsh land operations, with one or two notable exceptions, were able to proceed very largely according to plan.

On 9 June, the day after the *Sir Galahad* disaster and the associated losses at Fitzroy, a date when the war, in bitter winter weather, had just five more days to run, a *Scout* helicopter of 656 Squadron piloted by Ian Roy was en route to supply a Scots Guards platoon at Port Harriet House near Stanley. As he approached, the house was heavily shelled. The pilot held off out of range. When the shelling ceased, he approached a second time, but then came under *Blowpipe* fire himself. The first missile missed by about twenty-five yards but there is thought to have been a second. The Scotsmen later retrieved a large part of a *Blowpipe* casing and presented it to Roy as a memento.[23]

Not all were so lucky: the war in the South Atlantic cost 255 British lives and another 777 were wounded; the Argentinians had more than twice as many dead. On the missile log, *Rapier* initially claimed 14 enemy aircraft destroyed (with another 6 probable), *Blowpipe* 9 (plus another two probable), Sea *Dart* 8, *Seacat* 8 (plus another two probable) and Sea *Wolf* 5. The *Sea Harriers* claimed 16 aircraft downed with the *Sidewinder* (plus another probable) and four with cannon (plus another 2 probable).[24]

The argument over figures on air combat, because they emerge from the stress of battle, is without end. These initial totals were later inflated in some cases. But they indicate how relative performance was estimated. Aircrew were on both the firing and receiving ends of the guided weapons. Submitted to the unyielding absolutes of war for the first time, they learned the missiles' potential and their limitations. For Castlereagh the feedback from the Falklands was digested with due care and applied at once to the business of conceiving a new missile generation.

NOTES

1   Hugo Young: *One of Us* (London, 1991) p 264

2 Max hastings & Simon Jenkins: *The Battle for the Falklands* (London, 1983), p 71

3   Hastings & Jenkins, op.cit., p 11

4   Foreman, interview with author

5   Maurice McFadden, interview with author

6   Rodney Burden et al.: *Falklands – The Air War* (Dorset, 1987) p18

7   *Exocet* (London, 1983)

8   Hastings & Jenkins, op.cit., pp 159,206

9   Hugh Lyon: *Encyclopedia of the World's Warships* (London, 1978) p 66

10 Hugh Lyon, op.cit., p 250

11 Hastings & Jenkins, op.cit., p 211

12 Hastings & Jenkins, op.cit., pp 159,206

13 Hastings & Jenkins, op.cit. pp 208-9

14 Hastings & Jenkins, op.cit., p 221

15 Burden et al., op.cit., p 24

16 Hastings & Jenkins, op.cit., pp 214-215

17 Hastings & Jenkins, op.cit., p 244

18 Millar Crawford, interview with author

19 George Townend, interview with author; Hastings & Jenkins, op.cit., p 266

20 Julian Thompson: *No Picnic* (London, 1985) p 85

21 Julian Thompson, op.cit., pp90, 92

22 Hastings & Jenkins, op.cit., pp 280-281

23 Burden et al., op cit., p 350

24 Letter from the Minister of Defence Procurement, Geoffrey Pattie, MP, to Sir Philip Foreman, 2 August 1982

14

CLOAK AND DAGGER

THE experience of the Falklands brutally rammed home the importance of nations being careful to whom they sold their missiles. The task force in the south Atlantic might very well have been facing *Javelin*, *Blowpipe's* up-rated successor, which very narrowly missed the brief war. Essentially, it was designed to do the same job as *Blowpipe*, but more easily. The older missile, sold to twenty different forces in a dozen different countries, was not always simple to use. Some of the British troops deploying it in the Falklands only had time to acquire the most rudimentary knowledge of it. This was fair neither to the aimers nor to the weapon.

The war also imposed new rules of engagement. Aircraft had never flown so low so fast to the assault before. The Argentinian *Aeromacchi* came in so low over Fanning Head to bomb the frigate, *Argonaut*, on 21 May, 1982 that the crew of the vessel thought the aeroplane had plunged into the sea. It was the day of the dawn landing on the beach at San Carlos Water on East Falkland. As one petty officer testified, "We didn't see it until it was right on us." When the enemy *Mirages* and *Skyhawks* attacked the 45,000-ton *Canberra*, the *Blowpipe* operators on the upper decks faced aircraft coming in at a height of 50 feet. The Argentinian pilots lacked nothing in daring and quickly earned the respect of the British. One *Skyhawk* pilot, Alberto Philippi, confessed after the war that, coming in at 450 knots, he had had his altimeter set for 30 feet, causing the cockpit alarm to sound continuously. Using the surrounding hills as concealment, his and the other enemy aircraft became visible only seconds before pressing home their attack and were gone seconds later, the sky filled with the flashes of *Seacat*, *Blowpipe* and *Rapier* in confrontation.[1]

A year later, as arms dealers worldwide assembled to exploit their biggest shop window of all, the biennial Paris Air Show in June 1983, the gossip over the champagne in the chalets at Le Bourget was that Shorts' old lady, *Seacat*, was acquiring a new lease of life among the sixteen navies which had bought it long ago. Already dismissed by its critics as obsolescent, analysis of performance in the south Atlantic was leading, not to an accelerated phasing out, but to consideration of a multi-million pound ammunition order from the Royal Navy, much of it for the practice rounds required for regular test firing. By 1985, *Seacat* had achieved sales of £650m, helped by further replacement orders worth £10m. from New Zealand and an unnamed customer.

The Falklands also increased the international currency of *Blowpipe*. It was seen on news film and its use discussed. Its portability was something new. The sensitivity lay in the sinister potential should the weapon fall into the wrong hands; for it would enable a terrorist to destroy an airliner. Shorts had succeeded in policing its distribution with remarkable efficiency. But its very availability and relatively easy transport meant that it began to crop up in some unlikely, not to say embarrassing, places.

In distant Afghanistan there had been a military coup in 1978 in which the president of the young republic, Mohammed Daud, a cousin of the former King Zahir, was killed. A Marxist People's Democratic Party took office. Two further coups followed. In the second a puppet was put in place with Soviet aid. Russian troops moved in. But, encouraged by worldwide condemnation of the invasion, Afghan Islamic rebels in the hills, the Mujahidin, embarked upon a guerrilla campaign. In the early 1980s they armed themselves from the usual clandestine sources, including a not unwilling provider, the United States. Television news editors, who find wars and the resultant human desolation irresistible, smelt East-West confrontation and began to send correspondents.

It was at this stage that the guerrillas, pictured in action sequences in the mountains against the Russian forces, were seen on television screens firing missiles from the shoulder. The weapon was unmistakably *Blowpipe* and the missiles were being directed at Russian helicopters. There are pictures filed at Castlereagh, taken in bazaars in Kabul, in which the missile is clearly identifiable among hardware captured from the guerrillas and put on show by the Afghan government. It was also reported as having been seen on sale at the big arms bazaar at Darra run by an Islamic fundamentalist group in Pakistan.

No one is saying precisely how Blowpipe got into the hands of the Mujahidin. The fact that they had been supplied with "up to thirty" launchers and missiles was reported in August 1986, with the suggestion that they had reached the rebels through "Nigerian sources". Later a quantity was captured by a joint Soviet-Afghan sweep through rebel strongholds in Paktia province.[2]

When export licences are granted for foreign sales of British arms, an end-user certificate is normally required, designed to prevent selling on of the merchandise to an unapproved customer. But the secretive and very joined up world of the international arms dealer is difficult for governments to penetrate. In reality selling on is difficult to prevent. The only sanction the government of the manufacturing country possesses is the threat to withhold further supplies if unauthorised selling on is suspected. The United States, alone among foreign clients of British arms manufacturers, is not obliged to provide end-user certificates at all. This was confirmed by the Government in the House of Lords in April 1986.[3]

One subsidiary result of Mrs Thatcher's closeness to the Reagan administration was the bid – very nearly successful – by Colonel Oliver North, a short time before, to have 20 *Blowpipe* launchers supplied to the Contra rebels in Nicaragua. His proposal was that Ecuador, already a *Blowpipe* customer, should provide an end-user certificate. But it appears that he was required to clear the transaction with London as well as Washington and that, while Washington was keen to do the deal, London withheld approval.

What is established is that *Blowpipe* proved a lethal weapon on the Afghan-Pakistani border. Its targets were the helicopter gunships the Russian forces were using to move about in the difficult mountainous terrain of the old north-west frontier provinces between Kabul and Kandahar. According to one source a key factor was the guerrillas' penchant for firing up to three missiles simultaneously at the same target, tactics unknown in the Royal Artillery!

The first two successful downings of Russian helicopter gunships with *Blowpipe* were reported at Barikot, a garrison town near the frontier, in May 1987, by Yunis Khalis, leader of an Islamic fundamentalist sect. The Russian aircraft were equipped with hot infra-red flares to confuse the heat-seeking systems of the captured Soviet-made SA-7 missiles and the American *Stingers* the rebels were known to possess. But the gunships remained vulnerable to *Blowpipe*, whose line-of-sight optical tracking system was immune to the flares.

Mr Khalis had visited London three months before for talks at the Foreign Office. Most of the missiles going to Afghanistan seem to have gone to his party. A matter of weeks after his visit, one of his guerrilla commanders, Abdul Haq, met Mrs. Thatcher in Downing Street for talks believed to have been arranged through MI6. An Afghan source said afterwards that of course arms would have been discussed.

Haq is believed to have been in contact with MI6 in Pakistan from 1980 onwards. Peter Preece, an MI6 officer who served in Pakistan from 1982 to 1985 under the diplomatic cover of an embassy official, cultivated contacts with the guerrillas and is believed to have pushed the case for arming them. On returning to London, he was given an intelligence post in the Cabinet Office and would have been there when the talks with Khalis and Haq took place in Whitehall. The first *Blowpipes* arrived in Afghanistan about a month later.[4]

The deft hand of the CIA must have been involved in the supply of *Stingers* to the Mujahidin. It would have arranged the buying of the hardware from the manufacturer, General Dynamics, through the Department of Defense and also the delicate matter of delivery and

Javelin being brought ashore off Plymouth during exercises by the Royal Marines.

distribution in the field. Sources also suggest that the CIA was closely involved in the *Blowpipe* transaction.

One other case where the end-user provision did not always work was the enforcement of the British embargo which applied to arms for South Africa during the apartheid regime. The South African forces had long cast covetous eyes on Shorts' missiles, most keenly on *Tigercat*. In the end they succeeded in beating the embargo and getting them through the secret co-operation of a third party. *Tigercat* eventually emerged in the South Africans' armoury thinly disguised as the *Hilda* missile.

Both Jordan, the largely land-locked kingdom, abutting on the vast Saudi Arabian desert to the south-east and with the troubled Israeli frontier to the west, and Saudi Arabia itself had been negotiating to buy the American *Stinger*. But it became clear that neither deal was going to get Congressional approval. The powerful pro-Israeli lobby in Washington proved invincible and in March 1984 President Reagan duly vetoed Jordan's request for 1,600 *Stingers*. It was then leaked to the press corps accompanying the Queen and the Duke of Edinburgh on a visit to Amman that Hussein's government was negotiating a £90m deal for the much newer *Javelin* – which was not yet in service but which would soon be available. When Her Majesty returned to London, one of her first visitors was the Belfast-born Israeli president, Chaim Herzog, who came to lunch at Windsor, and was expected to invite the Queen to visit Jerusalem. Winning friends and influencing people was all part of the arms game.

Shorts, however, was to emerge triumphant from this maelstrom of competing interests. By the summer it was announced that sales of *Javelin* exceeded £120m. It had already been earmarked for the Army and it was about to enter service with the Royal Marines.

Northern Ireland's political instability in the 1970s and 1980s required constant vigilance by industrialists in sensitive sectors. In retrospect it is remarkable that the plant at Castlereagh emerged more or less unscathed from the cauldron of unrest seething beyond its walls. Civil order had to be maintained in a situation where political constraints governed the use of the Army. This meant that active republican terrorist cells were left largely undisturbed in the well-defined zones where they found it possible to impose their will. The most prominent were those in west Belfast, parts of County Tyrone and the border zone of south Armagh.

The Army policed these from heavily fortified posts equipped with heliports. All personnel and supplies were flown in to the rural outposts. Troops involved in patrols on the ground, particularly in the sensitive border zone, were dropped on the spot and later lifted out at pre-arranged rendezvous for return to post. As a result the Provisional IRA, which already had RPG rockets and Soviet-made SAM 7s, made consistent efforts to equip itself with short-range ground-to-air guided missiles. The targets were the Army helicopters which, in the exigencies of their task, were often obliged to fly at low altitude. Attacks were made on the aircraft with a variety of weapons and it was obvious that *Blowpipe* or *Javelin* would indeed be coveted by the keepers of the IRA armoury.

The Castlereagh plant was an IRA target on several occasions. Telephoned bomb scares, designed to disrupt production, became a nuisance in the later 1980s. There were even a couple of explosions. In July 1989 terrorists breached the perimeter fence. At the end of the year Alanbrooke Road, which provides the main access, was closed to external traffic by the Government and a new security fence three metres high was erected. The size and solidity of this barrier led to protests from local residents, but it was finally approved by the planning authorities in October 1990.

Events earlier in the year had guaranteed that there would be no relaxation in security. On 20 March 1990 a telephone warning was given that five bombs had been planted. Two devices later exploded, the first at 3 pm while the plant was still being evacuated. Four employees were taken to hospital suffering from shock. There was no damage to buildings, but a fuel tank and fencing were damaged. Hoax telephone warnings continued in the ensuing weeks, forcing evacuation of the factory. The main effect of these incidents was to disrupt output plans of the new *Starstreak* missile which was about to start production.

Loyalist terrorists also targeted the plant. On 31 October 1988 two armed men wearing blue overalls breached security and walked into the factory site by mingling with workers returning from their lunch break. The new facilities for *Starstreak* production being built meant that outside contractors were coming and going and the strangers' presence caused no comment. They made their way through two gates, into a building and up a hallway to a glass-panelled door through which they could watch a painter touching up what they thought was a *Javelin* aiming unit. While they waited they helped themselves to coffee from a machine in the corridor to provide a pretext for their presence.

When the painter left his place for a moment, one of the terrorists kept watch while the other darted inside and snatched the item from the bench. They were then challenged by an inspector; but one of the raiders produced a gun and both ran out of the building with their trophy and made off in a waiting car.

In fact all they had got was an operationally useless training model of the device; but, a short time before, the same painter had been touching up a fully-operational aiming unit of *Starstreak*, Castlereagh's newest and most sophisticated high-velocity weapon. It was a near miss for the raiders. Who were they? No one ever claimed the exploit, but detectives were convinced that the Ulster Defence Association or the Ulster Volunteer Force was involved. There was a feeling, indeed, that this was in part an inside job. The terrorists, significantly, knew exactly where to go to be likely to get what they wanted. Their only mistake was to grab a realistic mock-up of the real thing they sought - the *Javelin* aiming unit.

Two weeks later detectives mounted a number of raids and made arrests in the Markethill and Hamiltonsbawn districts of County Armagh, one police unit concentrating on a small housing estate at Loughgilly on the road between Markethill and Newry. The searches produced a rocket launcher with five warheads, rifles and grenades, more than 12,000 rounds of ammunition - and parts belonging to a *Javelin* aiming unit. The company quickly made clear that the parts in themselves were useless; nor did they relate to the stolen mock-up - which was never recovered. But the find, following the earlier theft, caused uneasiness lest loyalist terrorists had the makings of an assembled missile and launcher in other dumps. Red Ulster Resistance berets were found with the arms.[5]

The South African connection reared its head again in the early 1980s when, having failed to obtain *Blowpipe* hardware, the decision was taken to explore the possibilities of copycat engineering. But for this a full set of design and working drawings of the chosen missile would be essential. Clandestine approaches by the South Africans were made through Army contacts in Northern Ireland to obtain the secret design drawings of *Blowpipe*.

It had been announced in March 1984 that a new air defence battery was to be formed in the Belfast area as part of a UK-wide upgrading of anti-aircraft measures. The new battery was to be based at Newtownards, County Down with the 102 Air Defence Regiment, Royal Artillery and it would be equipped with *Javelin*. The significant feature of the Newtownards battery was that it was largely a volunteer detachment manned by local part-timers who had signed on with the Territorial Army. They must have included among their number right-wing sympathisers with the Afrikaaner cause, for Territorials from the battery eventually were persuaded to travel to a rendezvous with agents acting for the South Africans in Paris. But their movements were already being watched by British intelligence who secretly photographed them with the agents. The collaborators were caught in the French capital with *Blowpipe* missile parts and the incriminating papers relating to the missile in their possession.[6] The parts came from a non-operational missile which had been given to the Regiment by Shorts for teaching purposes. The Territorials from Newtownards turned out to be a sober group of solid citizens not at all cast in the mercurial espionage mould.

With the gradual liberalisation of the regime during the 1990s, the British arms embargo on South Africa was lifted and the republic no longer required to negotiate cloak and dagger transactions through third parties.

With commercially sensitive products like those produced at Castlereagh, of course, discretion was the essence of success. It was also true that who you knew could matter more than what you knew. So making a sale often depended upon making discreet contact with a strategically positioned acquaintance, encountered perhaps years before, and cards exchanged, over air show cocktails in Paris, Farnborough or Singapore; but whose direct-line and mobile phone numbers had been logged carefully in the fat leather-bound pocket book which, in the days before the laptop, was every salesman's passport to a crust.

A serious call not uncommonly would produce the response: "I can't take this now. In the office. Have to go round the corner." Whereupon the quarry might be seen making his way into the street and thence to Paddington Station, and an empty telephone box. It is a case where the spy film cliché tells the truth; for the motto in preserving confidence was to keep on the move and not to use the same land-line telephone all the time, because it could be tapped.

The need for this sort of undercover approach demanded a certain kind of salesman. He needed to have been around, to have met a lot of people, to be socially at ease in diverse cultures, and to be able to improvise with some resource and to look after himself when events took an unanticipated turn. As a rule in the 1980s this pointed to ex-officers. One Castlereagh engineer remarked that –

> You don't need to be a rocket scientist to sell our stuff. Well connected ex-officers mayn't know much about some of our products, but they often wear a nice silk handkerchief and matching tie. Sorry I sound a bit cynical, but if you knew somebody who went to Sandhurst who knew the prince of such and such a country, you'd have a much better entrée than Joe engineer who knows all about the weapons system and could talk about it for days.[7]

Since then things have changed somewhat. The customer is now inclined to be more discerning. But a military background is still an important confidence builder for the client. Ex-officers, after all, are people who have used weapons.

Alex Roberts came to Shorts in 1956 from the RAF. On the aircraft side, as test pilot, he had flown everything from the experimental VTOL SCI and English Electric *Canberra* jet bomber onwards. When he came to take charge of all Shorts' aircraft and missile sales and marketing, he possessed, unlike many of his sales colleagues in the business, a wide – ranging aviation background. He would have made no claim to missiles expertise; but what he was able to do was to open doors. As a premier member of the UK aerospace sales club, whose personnel travelled the world attending the same air shows, trade missions and weapons exhibitions, he had military connections worldwide. Much of the selling was very political, i.e., British weapons sold to former British territories and protectorates like Brunei and Jordan. The salesmen tended to meet the same people at the same places, whether it was Rolls Royce selling engines or Westland selling helicopters. A wide acquaintance was the result – and an exhaustive networking knowledge of buying trends in the arms market.

Roberts secured the *Javelin* sales in Oman. He also operated in Korea and Canada and made the early *Starburst* sales to Malaysia. Later, sitting on the board at Castlereagh from the time of the joint venture with Thomson in 1993, he exercised oversight of sales like the

Starburst contract in Kuwait after the Gulf War. The man on the ground in Kuwait was another ex-officer, Mike Stubington. He had the thankless task of camping in the Sheraton Hotel in Kuwait City for the 300 days after the war ended, until the *Starburst* contract was sealed. Meantime outside, the desert sun was obscured by the dense and stinking smoke from the oil wells fired by the retreating Iraqis. Stubington grumbled freely in the exhausting heat – and no one denied he was entitled to.

Many of these experienced arms salesmen would be assigned to cultivate a particular national market. They would be told not to come back until they had a contract in the bag. Not that that in most cases involved returning to Belfast. Shorts had its London office in the desirable purlieus of Berkeley Square and there were numerous well padded hostelries conveniently nearby.

Salesmen on the job had to be capable of negotiating overseas cultural shoals where waters, by long custom, were heavily tainted with bribery. Often, to be sure of a sale in the final stages, there was no option but to pay a sizeable commission to the agent who was the go-between with the client government. You did it because you knew your competitors were doing it – particularly the Americans. There the culture was highly formalised, with the US embassies on the spot, encouraged by the Pentagon, offering ready advice on whom to pay and how much. In the 1970s the US Securities and Exchange Commission in Washington uncovered the existence of slush funds within some very big players indeed: Exxon, Gulf, Northrop, Lockheed, Boeing and McDonnell Douglas. In 1975, one executive admitted that, in the preceding five years at least $22m. had been spent by his company on payments believed to have gone to "officials and political organisations" in foreign countries. These were later found to include Japan, Indonesia, Iran, Saudi Arabia, the Philippines, the Netherlands, Italy and possibly Germany. Adnan Khashoggi, the Saudi Arabian entrepreneur, had received $106m. in commissions alone. Prince Bernhard of the Netherlands had received $1m. – after writing demanding money. The existence of his two letters supported the plea of the manufacturers that they were the victims of extortion.[8]

A generation later, no one can say that bribes are no longer paid. It is most unlikely that they have ceased to have importance in the Third World. But there has been a tightening of corporate control at the top. The new policy adopted by Thomson-CSF when the French company assumed control of Castlereagh in 1999 is a case in point. It was resolved to revise the code of practice for marketing overseas. This meant that, as the then Chief Executive Officer, Terry Stone, explained –

> Thereafter negotiations with other governments would be open and there would be no inappropriate payments within the Thomson Group – no backhanders. This was quite a shock to some other companies. The

new rules effectively aimed to create a new culture. From the company's point of view, the old way was a way of trading in different parts of the world. If you wanted to do business there, you had to do it. We needed to clean up our act.[9]

The French Government, which in the 1970s had been cynically alleged to maintain a "Ministry of Bribes" as a sales incentive, moved, on foot of a European Commission initiative in the late 1990s, to make it a criminal offence to pay commissions to government officials. Thomson duly fell into line.

NOTES

1   Hastings and Jenkins, op. cit. pp. 203-5 Despite their daring, the pilots were also safer flying low. They presented more difficult missile and gunnery targets. Dive bombing would have been a more effective means of attack

2   *Jane's Defence Weekly, 23 August 1986*

3   Ministerial answer to Lord Kennet, House of Lords, 15 April 1986

4   *Independent, 20/21 May 1987*

5   *Belfast Telegraph, 1/5/16/17 November 1988*

6   *Belfast Newsletter,* 18 November 1986; *Belfast Telegrapb,* 27 March 1984; David Beatty, interview with the author

7   Interview with the author

8   Sampson, op.cit., pp271-8

9   Terry Stone, interview with author

15

FROM JAVELIN TO STARSTREAK

BLOWPIPE, tested in the Falklands, represented a key advance, introducing the first shoulder-launched, visually-guided weapon. But, after studying the feedback, the conclusion at Castlereagh was that it must be made easier to fire. The answer lay in keeping the *Blowpipe* airframe and adding a new guidance system. The important improvement was that this was semi-automatic, cutting down the training requirement for the young soldiers who would be using it. In fact, work on what was to become the *Javelin* was already under way before the war in the south Atlantic and the mobilisation of the task force. If hostilities had been prolonged a few months longer, the new missile might well have been at San Carlos Water.

The *Javelin* was a slender tube just under one and half metres long with fuses in the tip of the nose, in front of the guidance equipment. The warhead was in the centre section with the rocket motors behind. Four delta-shaped aerofoils were fitted in the nose to control attitude and four in the tail to provide stability. The system was made ready by clipping the aiming unit on to the canister holding the missile, an operation taking only five seconds.

The aiming unit had a pistol grip firing handle with a trigger at the right hand side. On the left there was an optical sight linked to a built-in video camera. When an attack was imminent, the operator switched on the system and fixed an aiming mark on the target

The radio controlled *Javelin* weapon system deployed and ready for action

in the sight by means of a thumb-controlled joystick. The target was tracked briefly, the safety catch released and the trigger pressed. This launched the missile from its canister by its first-stage motor and, at a safe distance and within a fraction of a second, it was boosted to

The *Javelin* missile exiting the launcher at over 70 mph prior to being boosted to supersonic speed by the second stage motor

supersonic speed by the second-stage rocket. The video camera detected flares from the missile and fed a digital signal to a microprocessor. The job of the processor was to calculate the flight correction required to bring the missile from its own track on to the operator's direct sightline to the target, i.e. the centre of the aiming mark. The processor's instructions were then fed to the missile by radio. Range was more than four kilometres.

Javelin was officially announced in September 1983, the culmination of long shifts and several weeks' 24-hour working at Castlereagh. The new weapon was well received by the Army. *Javelin's* radio link represented a big advance. With numerous channels the risk of jamming could be substantially reduced. The first production order was placed in 1984 and potential export customers started to ask questions. *Javelin* was later to sell to a dozen armed forces in seven different countries. There were several selling points: the number of practice rounds needed for *Blowpipe* was cut by almost 50 per cent. There was a more powerful warhead and the second-stage rocket

Javelin being fired from a Vehicle Multiple Launcher by one of the Middle Eastern customers

motor was increased to give additional range. But the use of miniature electronics and computerisation to provide the semi-automatic guidance system was the big leap forward. The aimer's task was made much easier and the weapon rendered more deadly.

But missile targets were also becoming more menacing and even *Javelin* was susceptible to countermeasures. It still involved sending a radio signal from the ground to tell the missile where to go and the Soviet technology was capable of jamming the signal. In addition, the velocity of the *Blowpipe-Javelin* airframe was limited. The maximum achievable was about Mach 1.4, about 1,100 mph, a formidable speed, but not considered adequate for the weapon needed to take on the new assault helicopters, well armoured, with pop-up capability and the ability to stand off, loosing missiles of their own at ground positions. As George Jackson put it,

> By the mid-1980s it was apparent that the next major battlefield threat for the close air defence weapon would be the late-unmasking armoured helicopter, greatly reducing the engagement time. Existing weapons would not be very effective against this type of target.[1]

The Cold War in the early 1980s still held diplomacy in its frigid vice. The Berlin Wall was intact and the desperate souls who sought to scale it were shot like dogs. Gorbachev, *glasnost* and *perestroika* were several years away. Russian forces had just invaded Afghanistan. Within the Soviet colossus, dissension was still regarded as a threat to be ruthlessly suppressed. In the satellite states the will of Moscow was rigidly enforced. In Poland the Solidarity trade union under Lech Walesa was banned, its leaders imprisoned and martial law imposed. Round the world the number of Soviet spies, masquerading as diplomats and expelled from non-communist countries, mounted steadily: 27 in 1981, 49 in 1982 and 147 in 1983. These figures speak for themselves. Defence technology was becoming ever more complex. NATO had begun to pool its intelligence. The top priority of the KGB and the GRU was to catch up with the West and to keep abreast of both civil and military advances.[2]

The vulnerability of *Javelin* to jamming by the ever-advancing sophistication of electronic countermeasures inspired such a mood of urgency in Government that a rare and secret document from Whitehall arrived one day on the desk of Bob Manvell, the Castlereagh Divisional Director in charge of the Missile Systems Division. It was an Operational Emergency Requirement, in a category known in the business as "eyes only". Its key question was how quickly Castlereagh could come up with a design, something that could not be jammed, to meet the new challenge. Manvell passed the paper to his Chief Engineer, Charles Raitt-Brown, who called in Jimmy McIlroy, Head of Weapon Systems Electronics. From these consultations the whole concept of employing a laser beam to provide the line of sight guidance was born. The laser, an acronym of Light Amplification by Stimulated Emission of Radiation, is a device whereby the physicist can project a high-intensity beam from solids, liquids or gases. The key attribute of a laser-guided missile would be that its guidance system could not be jammed. Put crudely, the aimer would point the narrow laser beam at the aircraft target. The missile, when fired, would follow the line of the beam.

Meantime the Future Projects Department headed by Dick Ransom, another of Conway's innovative engineers, was carrying out a research study, partly financed by the RAE, into an Advanced Man Portable Anti-aircraft Weapon System (AMPAWS). From this was to emerge Castlereagh's life-saving ticket to the future, the High Velocity Missile – HVM. Test firings took place in 1983 and 1984, enabling the Guided Weapons Division to position itself to advantage for the key contractual battle now to come.

While research was forging ahead, the Thatcher Government was pushing its free-market philosophy. The Prime Minister let it be known that henceforward the norm in defence procurement would be competition. Millar Crawford, Chief Executive Officer of Thales Air

Defence, was to be closely involved in the assimilation of the Government's new thinking at the plant. Coming to Shorts as a young mechanical engineering graduate from Queens University, he had been personal assistant to Bob Manvell for four years in the early 1980s.

> There was the quite new concept of having a prime contractor. The competition for the High Velocity Missile was one of the first where the Ministry was saying – you take full responsibility for everything. Previously they would have purchased the missile from us, the vehicle from the vehicle supplier, the launcher from someone else and then paid someone to integrate the system. Peter Levene, as he was then, had taken charge of the Procurement Executive. He seemed to be saying – "We'll have this prime contractor and they'll be totally responsible and they'll be paid the reward for taking the risk." Value for money was the theme.[3]

The practical effect on Castlereagh was to push the factory into direct competition for the crucial HVM with British Aerospace. Each was given a Project Definition Contract. Only one could win.

David Beatty, Director of Strategy for the company, and Sales Director for both the United Kingdom and the United States, who had joined Castlereagh as a student apprentice in 1981, explained the impact of Thatcherism –

> In the 1980s we'd thought this very short range close air defence weapons system was ours by birthright. The first time anyone said it's not, and challenged that, was the procurement decision on the HVM. We had to go through a very intense competition against BAE Systems. They were the *Rapier* boys and their whole plan was: "Let's kill this Shorts lot dead. If we can keep our *Rapier* in the line and we can make a move on this close air defence job, then we can have this thing stitched up for the next thirty years." [4]

Shorts, as a Government-owned enterprise sited in a high-unemployment zone, was exposed on two counts - and each was used freely in the fight. Would the Government merely favour its own, at the same time yielding to pressure to place the work where the jobs were needed most?

In fact the same battle had been fought a year or so before. Shorts had entered a redesign of the Embraer *Tucano* from Brazil in the competition to provide a new trainer aircraft for the RAF. The rival bidders were whittled down from nearly twenty to two. Shorts' opposition in the last round had been a version of the Swiss-designed Pilatus PC9. The *Tucano* won. The big losers were Pilatus – and British Aerospace, who were to do half the work for the Swiss in their factory at Prestwick in Ayrshire. The residual bitterness was shown in the aftermath. The Pilatus was promoted at the Paris Air Show of 1985 as the aircraft the RAF wanted, but was not allowed to have; while murmurs of sour grapes were to be heard from Shorts' hospitality suite nearby. This was not all: it was suggested by the losers that the *Tucano's* engine was unsuitable for the job. The contract was condemned as an employment measure for Northern Ireland and a payback to the Brazilians for help on the long supply line to the south Atlantic during the Falklands War.[5]

This, then, was the charged climate in which, mere months later, Shorts crossed swords with BAe for a second time. The omens were for a tough fight. Michael Heseltine, Defence Secretary, had boasted that the *Tucano* competition had reduced bid prices by 35 per cent. The Shorts' bid had won, he said, because it was clearly cheaper. Accordingly, Castlereagh resolved to adopt similarly aggressive tactics in the bid for the HVM, as Beatty outlined –

> We decided to be very flamboyant about the whole thing – to fire some prototype missiles, do a very good proposal. It was the first time we did a proposal in the form of a video - which was really going some. The competition lasted about a year, from the back end of 1984 to the end of '85.

> We had to put a proposal together which showed that we were better than this lot in England; and Foreman made us establish a very aggressive price. He said the only way you're going to win this is with a very attractive price. It was a steal for the Government. They got awfully good value for money. That's why we had to spend some of our own money to make sure we could deliver.[6]

In the end it took Castlereagh £100m. of its own money to win the HVM job. This was the first major fixed-price contract Castlereagh had had: but it was still worth £225m., covering development and production of the first tranche of missiles and launcher systems which were to become *Starstreak*. It was the Programmes Department under George Townend which undertook the direct dealing with the Procurement Executive of the Ministry of Defence –

> At the end of the exercise what we produced was an enormous heap of documentation. It defined every little bit of the job – training and everything else. The final delivery of the data was quite enormous. . a crate three feet wide by six feet long. The Ministry then called us to a meeting in a dank and dusty basement in some Ministry building in London. We wouldn't have been surprised to see rats running about it! And there we were interrogated by the assembled experts, the Services included, as to how we'd do this and do that. Put us through the mill. Then eventually we heard we were chosen.[7]

The final bid was largely put together by one of Townend's Programme Managers, Bill Black, who became Programme Manager for Starstreak in 1985, and by Chris Melrose, Commercial Manager. The bottom line was the truth that, if the bid had failed, Castlereagh

The new plant designed specifically to accommodate the new breed of missiles

(Below) Inside the new manufacturing facility during fitting out in 1990

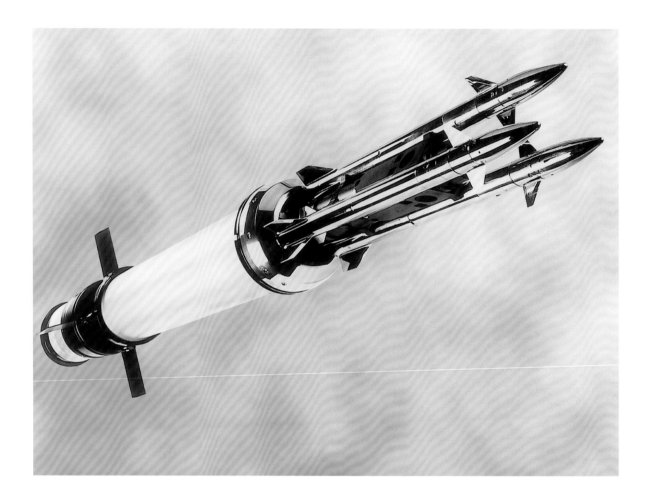

The *Starstreak* missile with its three laser guided darts

would not exist today. Most important, the £100m. which was to be spent proved to be a very shrewdly calculated risk. By this spending, the seed corn was planted which, with good husbandry, would still be yielding harvests a generation ahead. Included was a new plant to make the missile, coupled with new tools and new procedures. "We had to have a brand new facility," said Crawford –

> With brand new concepts and brand new trade union agreements. We had to have a new way of thinking, a new philosophy, if we were going to manufacture the HVM to cost – and that was what was supported through Bombardier. The day we won the HVM was the day we were committed to that investment. If you'd tried to manufacture the product in the conventional way, the losses would have been horrendous.[8]

People on each job were given more individual responsibility, doing their own inspection. It was Tokyo come to Castlereagh. All this was vital to success. Sir Philip Foreman, in retrospect, views the decision as opening the gateway into a new kind of engineering world –

The new *Starstreak* factory at Castlereagh was the last capital expenditure I authorised before I retired. It was. . is . . a superb factory and inside it the equipment and the sort of work they're doing is unbelievable. They're working to tolerances we thought were impossible – to tenths of a thousandth of an inch.[9]

The new factory had 35 air handling units which changed the air eight and half times every hour, excluding any particle larger than .02 of a micron – one millionth of a metre.   John Leighton, Operations Production Manager, had 400 kw of heat to disperse, most of it from the machinery on the 130,000 sq, feet (33,000 sq, metres) of factory floor. "This was a very expensive operation," he stressed, "but a new combined heat and power unit has enabled us to reclaim the heat to use it to generate 80kw of free power."

Shorts Missile Systems were first awarded BS EN ISO 14001 accreditation for Environmental Management in late 1997 Front Row: Terry Stone, Chief Executive Officer and David Stewart, Director, Quality

Advances in technology saw the size of the roll position gyroscope reduce from that of *Seacat* to the *Starstreak* miniaturised one. (Incidentally the 50p piece was designed by H G Conway)

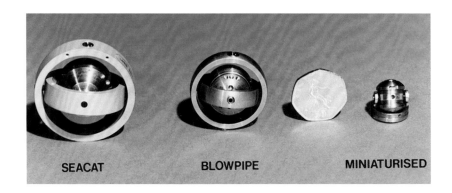

SEACAT   BLOWPIPE   MINIATURISED

Starstreak was born in the Future Projects Department in the late 1970s. First deliveries to the Army were made in the early 1990s. It is projected to be in service with the British Armed Forces beyond 2020 - a minimum 35-year span. In conception it has proved to be a remarkable feat of engineering, adaptable to ground-to-air, air-to-air and ground-to-ground use. Whereas *Javelin* represented the evolution of the earlier *Blowpipe* (flight time 20 seconds to 5 km), Starstreak (flight time 6 seconds to 5 km) is a phenomenon existing on an entirely new plane. Its velocity is in the region of Mach 3.5 - about 2,660 mph or, if you prefer, about 1,200 metres a second. This is achieved virtually instantaneously, i.e., in less than half a second, in air temperatures of 60 degrees Centigrade or minus 30. In practical

The *Starstreak* Lightweight Multiple Launcher provides a reversionary application for this versatile missile

terms it means the projectile travels three kilometres in three and a half seconds. Or in layman's terms, the missile leaves the launcher at more than 200 mph and in less than half a second is travelling at over 2,500 mph. Effective range, "about six kilometres", is in the upper limit for a close-range weapon.

Starstreak is sealed in a canister which also contains the two-stage rocket motor. The first stage launches the missile from the canister. The other, once the missile is at a safe distance from the launcher, boosts it to more than three times the speed of sound in a fraction of a second. As the second-stage motor burns out, three darts with stabilising fins in the tail and aerofoils in the nose peel off from the motor unit. Each contains a miniature gyroscope and circuitry which guide it along a coded laser beam to the target.

There is now a broad choice of options for the launcher. The lightweight tripod launcher with three missiles can even be air-dropped and, once at the launch point, can be set up in two minutes. In action, detection of target to pressing the trigger is specified to take less than two seconds. The sighting system, with its optical sight and control unit and own power supply, clips to the launcher column. From this the target is tracked and the laser beam projected. The laser guidance system is immune to all known countermeasures. An infra red camera can be mounted for use after dark.

A servo-driven turret with six missiles can be mounted in the back of a pick-up truck with the operator's console stationed up to 100 metres away. Equipped with a thermal camera and automatic target tracker, once the target is acquired and the trigger pressed, the system is completely automatic. The *Starstreak* heavier tracked and armoured vehicle, in the light tank mode, is in service with the British Army with eight missiles ready to fire on the launcher and stowage for up to a dozen further rounds. Air-to-Air *Starstreak* turns the tables, in the sense that it is designed to arm the low-flying attack helicopter which *Starstreak* itself was first conceived to combat. The system consists of a two-round missile launcher which can be fitted most notably to British versions of the American Apache AH64. Linked to the helicopter's radar, it can engage targets beyond six kilometres range.

But it took the Castlereagh team, 1,300 to 1,500 strong, nearly ten years to perfect *Starstreak*, from the drawing board to prototypes, through trials to safe certification. Hill Wilson, as Chief Systems Engineer, is recognised as an expert on the high-velocity missile. He had to confront some low moments. There were two basic difficulties: the project was tremendously demanding technically - and everyone at Castlereagh knew that, in the last analysis, they were out there on their own, exposed in territory where no one had ventured before. David Beatty replaced Bill Black as Programme Manager on *Starstreak* in 1987 and, with Wilson, pushed the project through to design certification and into production by 1992 –

Starstreak can provide the Apache helicopter with a much needed self defence capability

(Inset below) The lightweight system, which can be fitted to a wide range of vehicles, provides a fire and forget system capability

The *Starstreak* missile being fired from the *Stormer* vehicle during a British Army firing camp at Ustka in Poland

87KJ39

Roy McNulty had followed Foreman as Managing Director and I remember there were times when he and Raitt-Brown were being told at very senior level committees at the Ministry of Defence that we were very close to being telephoned to cancel the contract. We tried to get expertise in from the Continent, from America, other stranger places; but it was always quite evident that we were breaking new ground. No one had ever done anything like this.[10]

Subcontractors, though, provided yeoman support. In a sophisticated product like the supersonic missile, the main fabricator will make perhaps 20 per cent. The other 80 per cent. will be bought in from highly specialised providers. Their machine shops were hundreds of miles from Castlereagh, perhaps more. This required exceptional vigilance because a mistake at a critical moment could halt the whole project – and mistakes were made.

The launch of Starstreak to the export market, held at the Imperial War Museum in London

Soldiers of the Malaysian Armed Forces with the *Starburst* system. Seen here fitted with an Image Intensifier

The financial load of developing the HVM in the later 1980s tempted Castlereagh into a venture which some of those involved refer to as ending in catastrophe. In eagerness to sell the new missile abroad, potential customers, carefully selected, were invited to visit the test range where the development programme was in progress. The idea was to get in early, to telescope the sales process. But there were one or two unmitigated disasters. On one occasion the embryonic Starstreak, having been given a big preliminary boost before two senior American Senate advisers, nose-dived into the ground when the launcher failed to elevate at a test firing. Of course it worked well the second time and the blip passed by as just one more item in the long battle to sell Starstreak in the United States. Starstreak, of course, could not yet be making money.

In 1994 Millar Crawford was to assume overall responsibility for the contract as Director, *Starstreak*. It was a moment, he admitted, when "the programme wasn't going too good –

> The point was reached where the customer was losing confidence. The missile wasn't achieving the performance level. In 1994 we embarked on a two to three-year programme of literally having to rethink the project, the aerodynamics. The technology available to us in terms of wind tunnels had much improved. In the early days we'd been denied access to a high-velocity tunnel because of concern we might damage it. Now we could use tools that gave us the answers. The big challenge with Starstreak was that it flew so fast for such a short time, you weren't sure what it was doing aerodynamically.[11]

The two or three years of what was known in the plant as the *Starstreak* improvement programme (and in Ministry of Defence as the recovery programme) culminated in customer firings at one of the Army's Scottish firing ranges early in 1997. The presentation, at West Freugh on the shore of Luce Bay south of Stranraer, was an impressive success. Seven rounds were fired and all 21 darts hit the target. The Ministry, the key customer, was convinced that the "recovery" programme in their eyes had been fulfilled.

Conveniently, *Starburst*, the guise under which the *Javelin* S15 was promoted on the export market, was, and remains, popular abroad because no one could jam the laser guidance system. In the early stages of *Javelin's* uprating, though, the S15 was a top secret product and there was no question of export licences being considered. So far as officialdom was concerned, the S15 did not exist. But it pleased the Army and discreet inquiries began to be made by friendly forces abroad. It was duly deployed in the Gulf in 1991 (though not fired in anger) and was commended afterwards for achieving a reliability record of 100 per cent. availability on all battlefield days. This was notable (the word the Ministry of Defence used was "unprecedented") in an era when the alleged inadequacies of military

equipment often lead to sustained grumbling in the Services. The Army's self-loading rifle is a favourite source of contention. Tanks break down. Boots leak.

The consensus is that *Starburst* should still be in service in 2010. The Gulf certainly helped its sales. Kuwait, feeling vulnerable after the Iraqi invasion and warm towards the British, was one client. The missile was sold primarily as a multi-round system supported on a lightweight launcher.

The Americans, not without reason, were described within Castlereagh as the proprietors of the biggest protectionist market worldwide. Missile-wise, the Americans still put a great deal of trust in General Dynamics' veteran weapon, *Stinger*, now owned by Raytheon. Its critics condemn it as old technology: all right so long as its quarry is high up in the blue sky, but not very good with low-level targets. In the case of an aircraft down over the trees where hot smoke is coming out of a cottage chimney, *Stinger* will be in difficulty: it would not be able to distinguish between the two.

Indeed experience shows that the intensely nationalist American buying policy is capable of being breached – if a good enough case can be made. Shorts' success with the STOL *Sherpa* military transport, sold to the US Army in the 1980s, showed it. So did the more than

Starburst was first unveiled during Operation Desert Storm in the deserts of Saudi Arabia

The Kuwaiti team on completion
of the practice firing camp at
Manorbier in South Wales

one hundred British Aerospace *Harrier* jets bought by the US Marine
Corps in the 1970s; not to mention the English Electric *Canberra*
bombers built for the USAF and the Vickers *Viscount* turboprops
bought by civil airlines in the US in the mid-1950s.

But Castlereagh was well aware that it would be essential to enlist
Congressional backing to sell *Starstreak* to the United States. The way
to get it would be to demonstrate that, far from robbing senators' or
representatives' constituents of jobs, such a deal would provide new
ones. To do that, a suitable American company had to be found which
would manufacture the missiles under licence. Castlereagh eventually
settled upon Lockheed Martin, a company representing the
amalgamation of two of America's busiest defence contractors.

The Martin Company had built more than 400 of the British
Canberra bombers under licence at its Baltimore plant. It knew the
potential of this kind of work - if the product was right. Glenn Luther
Martin was one of the proud names in American aviation between the
World Wars. He led his company for 40 years. But the company's
post-war aircraft designs had only limited success. He retired in 1952
and his successor, George Bunker, with no background in planemaking,
had been more interested in the potential of missiles and anxious to
expand the company's stake in their manufacture. As for Lockheed, it

ranked in the top one hundred US industrial corporations and was a defence contractor on a massive scale. In the 1980s it was responsible for the US Navy's entire ballistic missile programme.[12] It was under these impressive auspices that Castlereagh said in 1994 that it would channel its *Starstreak* contract, were the Americans to buy. David Beatty explained that, from the early 1990s, the campaign was concentrated upon having the missile accepted by the Americans for fitting to their *Apache* helicopter –

> When the UK decided to buy the Apache from the US, the Americans agreed at a very senior political level to do a fair evaluation of *Starstreak* against *Stinger*. It takes a long time to get some of these programmes off the ground. But in America we've received over fifty million dollars in funding . . Congressional funds given to the US Army. We did the first stage tests in 1995-96 and the second phase in 1997- 98.

> Funding release and approval in America is always very protracted. But the tests so far have been 100 per cent. successful. The key thing is we haven't been out in the desert yet to shoot off against the *Stinger*. It indicates the length of time these things take. It's an extraordinarily difficult market and the only reason we persevere is if you get in there as a fit on a helicopter like *Apache* you'll be in there for ten years.[13]

Kuwaiti students during classroom training on the *Starburst* system in Belfast.

Assembly of part of the *Starstreak* guidance system in the ultra clean area in the new facility

Starstreak exports are still in their infancy. There are some potential customers in the offing. South Africa, for example, has chosen the missile. But the development cycle of the revolutionary weapon has included some thin years for Castlereagh, with profits from old marques declining and the big new one not yet available for world sale. So much so that the question began to be asked in the early 1990s whether Castlereagh could survive.

NOTES

1 George Jackson, unpublished memoir

2 Komitet Gosudarstevennoy Bezopasnosti (the Soviet Security Service) and Glavnoye Razvedyvatelnoye Upravleniye (the Chief Intelligence Directorate of the Army General Staff) shared Soviet espionage responsibilities; John Barron, op.cit., pp452-3; Christopher Dobson and Ronald Payne: *The Dictionary of Espionage* (London, 1984) p xiv

3 Millar Crawford, interview with the author

4 David Beatty, do.

5 *Financial Times*, 22 March 1985; author's private information

6 Beatty, do.

7 George Townend, do.

8 Crawford, do

9 Sir Philip Foreman, do

10 Beatty, do

11 Crawford, do

12 Bill Gunston: The Planemakers (London, 1980) pp59, 61-3

13 Beatty, do.

16

The French Connection

Since 1989 Bombardier of Montreal had been in ultimate control of Castlereagh. The old Missile Systems Division, which had succeeded Precision Engineering in 1969, became the Defence Systems Division, marking the sale of Short Brothers plc to the Bombardier Group. But the Canadian group's involvement was substantially in civil aircraft and railway rolling stock. It was not a missile, or even a defence, concern. But it was willing enough to sustain *Starstreak* in the meantime because it could appreciate the potential of the product. The Canadian armed services had been good customers for Castlereagh from the days of *Blowpipe* in the early 1970s, all the way through to the Gulf in 1991. Shortly before that campaign was launched, the telephone rang at Castlereagh one Thursday in 1990. It was the Canadians' logistics people to say they had a *Lockheed C130* transport going through to the Gulf in the following week. Could they stop in Belfast to top up their missile supplies? The contract was negotiated and signed on the Friday and the missiles packed on the Saturday. The *Hercules* duly landed at RAF Aldergrove on Sunday and collected a consignment of *Javelin* rounds.[1]

Responding to this kind of international challenge was one thing, close involvement with the defence industries quite another; and Bombardier's Canadian shareholders included an element which was not keen on it. Nor did the group as a whole have any intimate expertise in the very specialised, government-controlled arms markets Castlereagh sought to penetrate. Millar Crawford was aware that Bombardier did not really understand the peculiar intricacies of the defence business –

> They did refurbishment of the Lockheed Martin F16 fighter bomber and they had a spy-in-the-sky autogiro. But their aim at that stage wasn't to be at the leading edge of technology. They wanted to be the technology exploiters, not technology leaders; and they've been extremely good at that. But *Starstreak* was the leading edge: sometimes we thought it was beyond it. But it was an area where you couldn't easily put your slide rule. You didn't have the technical answers.

Opposite: The Thales Air Defence Headquarters in Belfast

How long will it take you to develop this? We didn't really know! Who're you talking to? We're talking to NASA .. to research establishments at the end of the Soviet Union. There isn't a reference point. We are the leading edge – the cutting edge. We're writing the rule book. They didn't feel comfortable with that.[2]

In fact the Canadians were looking round already, in the late 1980s, to see whether there was a suitable party who might be ready to help share the immediate investment load at Castlereagh and might be an eventual buyer. Terry Stone, who was to become Chief Executive officer at Castlereagh in 1993, and his colleague, Charles Raitt-Brown, had been looking for a potential partner even before Bombardier arrived to buy Shorts from the Government.

Stone, by training an electronics engineer, had a background in the space programme. He had worked on the *Polaris* missile project with Marconi at Portsmouth and Cammell Laird at Birkenhead, where the submarines were built; and had spent three years with Messerschmitt Bolkow Blohm at Munich between 1972 and 1975. Later, in California, he was concerned with liaison between the Germans and NASA. He subsequently returned to England to work on the European Space Agency satellite at Hawker Siddeley (eventually to become part of British Aerospace) and later on broadcast satellite development for the BBC and British Telecom. In 1984 he joined Shorts, becoming the company's Executive Director of Engineering and Quality in its last months in Government ownership.

Stone and his previous superior, Raitt-Brown, with their background in the upper reaches of the hugely larger world of British Aerospace, knew that total reliance on a single product, however promising, could not be sustained indefinitely. Put bluntly, Castlereagh needed a partner for survival.

But the short-to-medium-range missile business, although it involves some impressive and formidable micro-engineering concerns, is a small field. It is also highly specialised and technically exotic. So the chosen partner had to be drawn from a select circle. It included Raytheon, British Aerospace and Lockheed Martin, plus Matra and Thomson-CSF of France. A series of informal talks took place and in 1992 Thomson-CSF began to emerge as the favoured choice. The French concern attracted, first, because the French industry generally had been on a strong growth curve during the 1980s. But Thomson itself also had the appearance of being a good fit – and the appreciation, as would be essential, was to prove mutual.

Thomson was deeply into radars and into command, control and launcher systems, i.e., the brains, guidance and navigation processors of the hypersonic missile; but in its formidable array of plants scattered round the fringes of Paris it had no missile production facility of its own. It was making missile components; but there was no final integration, testing and design ownership of a stand-alone product.

That was the province of rival guided weapons contractors in France: Matra of Velizy-Villacoublay near Versailles and Aerospatiale at Chatillon and Bourges, since united with British Aerospace Dynamics to form the largest missile manufacturer, MBDA.

Allied within the large Thomson-CSF organisation, Castlereagh saw itself producing the missiles while Thomson provided the systems. As a potential bonus, additional contracts from France might come its way. As David Beatty explained it, Castlereagh dressed its shop window well –

> No one knew at that stage whether we could ever do it. I remember taking a lot of French fellows to watch *Starstreak* firings and they fell for the whole thing. Here we have a company that has invested a lot in its plant, with a new factory, a brand new missile, a captive work force with high levels of skills, and still its cost base was low; and with the leadership of people like Charles Raitt-Brown and Terry Stone, we were forward thinking. We took a lot of them along to see a missile being fired. The acceleration and velocity just had these guys bemused. How they ever came to say, yes, we'll go with this one....but I think they said yes for good business reasons, that it's a good partnership to buy into.[3]

The deal was formally signed early in 1993 after detailed negotiations which had lasted eighteen months. The transaction, in fact, represented a gleam of light in dark days; for the early 1990s were a difficult time for Castlereagh. The dismantling of the Berlin Wall in 1989, almost a generation after its construction, signalised the relaxation of tension in central Europe. As the fresh air of liberalism began to blow across the once-imprisoned satellite states and eventually within the Soviet Union itself, standing armies were reduced and NATO garrisons stood down. One of the first consequences was a reduction in defence budgets.

This time also marked the arrival of Shorts' Missile Systems Limited as a legal entity, owned in half shares by the parties in a joint venture company. The future of the enterprise had been safeguarded and Bombardier had a new partner to share mounting materials costs and investment and marketing – in a business where there could be a long interval of years between accepting a contract and receiving the last stage payment. The Canadians had injected new financial skills to Shorts' management which rubbed off on Castlereagh as well between 1989 and 1993. They were to prove excellent financial managers, experts in the business process. The importance of the £100m. of investment in the missile enterprise authorised by Bombardier cannot be overestimated: £35m. of it provided Castlereagh's new showpiece plant. It at once set the seal on the business and, by increasing its attractiveness to a desirable partner, provided the ticket to survival.

But the process was not without pain. Between 1994 and 1996, employment at Castlereagh was cut brutally from 1,500 to 500 people. The bulk of the development work on *Starstreak* was finished. There was no immediate new programme to replace it. The export market was quiet. The figures spoke for themselves. Castlereagh was turning over some £50m. a year; but, in one twelve-month period at this time, losses amounted to between £15m. and £20m.

The process of retrenchment began with early retirements. But that could not be enough. Some 450 of the Castlereagh team were highly-qualified, often very specialised engineers, difficult to replace if they were required again. Many good people were to lose their jobs. The exercise involved an organisational rebuild of the enterprise, from its surviving kernel, on a much lower cost basis. As Castlereagh began passing some of its recently acquired Canadian financial expertise on to the French, by 1995 the plant was again making money.

In parallel with the presence of French personnel at Castlereagh, a small joint company, some fifty strong, was set up in 1993 in Paris, Thomson-Shorts Systèmes. It was designed primarily as a vehicle for the sharing of technology and business practices and David Beatty was sent over from Belfast to get it up and running. He was sceptical whether his French colleagues managed to grasp everything that was said to them in the distinctive spoken English favoured in Northern Ireland. But professional relationships bonded profitably.

In the circumstances the complementary roles of Castlereagh and Thomson drove the new partners towards ever closer co-operation, while Bombardier's lack of involvement in the rarefied world of defence procurement emphasised the highly-specialised separation of its branch factory.

Thomson had the resources necessary to buy and was impressed with the technology. It could foresee the advantages of total ownership. In an air-show hospitality chalet, rent by the deafening crescendo of gas turbines above the Salon du Bourget in Paris in 1999, the talks between the parties were sealed. Glasses were raised, acknowledging the agreement by both that Castlereagh should pass into the full ownership of the French group. Castlereagh marked the turn of the century by delivering its 70,000th missile. Crawford, who left the company early in 1997, 18 months before the deal with Thomson-CSF was signed, recognised that the plant would be more comfortable as part of a defence business, rather than being isolated in another where its personnel were regarded as "those quirky missile people" who had a language and technology of their own –

We were those oddities – our business was different. Our customers were different. Our product was different. We were different. Whereas within Thomson the customer base would be the same, the technical language would be the same. That's what we mean by comfortable. It's an industry where our customers are governments and the decision makers are politicians and bureaucrats. It's a different mind-set.[4]

Thales, providing integrated air defence by the provision of the *Clara* radar and the automatic missile fire unit, Aspic

Some months later in 2000, Thomson-CSF changed its official designation to Thales, adopting the name of the wide-ranging Greek scientist and astronomer who succeeded in predicting a solar eclipse in 585 BC and was a pioneer in the study of stellar navigation. The sale of Castlereagh represented the opening of vast new horizons before it, for Thales was a global player – and growing, with total employment of some 64,000, 14,000 of those in other parts of the United Kingdom. Thales was already number two in British defence electronics and laying claim to be the main player in Europe in defence and aerospace electronics. Elsewhere, its total of more than 200 companies was scattered over 50 countries.

The impact upon the status of Castlereagh was immediate. Overnight the enterprise was elevated from a missile producer to one able to offer missile systems, radar-based surveillance and command control systems. *Martha*, *Samantha* and *Clara* radar and command control joined the Castlereagh stable and have been sold abroad. So has *Aspic*, a launcher system.

Diversification was the key objective in the second half of the 1990s. The most signal vindication of the new strategy was the invitation from the vast American defence electronics group, Raytheon, in 1998 to be its prime partner in the United Kingdom in their bid to provide the new air-to-air missile for the Eurofighter *Typhoon*, an aircraft project in which BAE Systems, Castlereagh's old rivals, British Aerospace, also re-named, were heavily involved. This was a notable accolade. If Castlereagh had ever wondered in the past whether it had really arrived among the grown-ups, this was confirmation: for the contract would be worth perhaps £1bn. The opposition came from a European consortium offering the *Meteor*. But decisions such as these are not made on purely technical grounds. Political horse-trading is heavily involved. David Beatty is convinced this was one such example –

> We lost - I think unfairly. Blair made the decision on political grounds. He chose the *Meteor*, not because it was the best price or the best risk, but to paper over the cracks in relations with the Europeans. We were offering an American design, derivative of a current product, low risk, lower cost and would have been lovely work for us. But a lot of decisions had been made by the Brits in recent years in going American. The *Apache* helicopter for the Army was one of them. The Prime Minister faced a lot of clamour from the European missile and electronics lobby against another American product. He was under duress to go European. This one was made to keep the politicians happy in Europe.[5]

But Castlereagh learned a great deal from bidding at the top table, as main nominated contractor for the United Kingdom. The chequered story of the Eurofighter, of course, is well known, a tale of rising costs and technical delays making it more than four and a half years late. The *Meteor* contract ran into similar delays, as British, French, Germans and Swedes sought to co-ordinate their policies.

In the meantime Castlereagh won a competition to build a missile, *VT1*, which is the European competitor of the British Aerospace *Rapier*. For this they offered an American design, sold by its originators, the Vought Company, to Thomson-CSF in 1998. It has a range of 11 kms. and a velocity of Mach 3.5 and has since been chosen by several forces, including both the French Navy and Air Force. This work was originally intended to be done in France by the French. Castlereagh had to fight hard to get it. It is another step towards broadening the base and securing the future.

Not so many years before, such a truly international enterprise as Thales would not have been possible. The Government of France still held a two-thirds controlling interest in Thomson-CSF in the mid-1990s and was intensely jealous of where its advanced technology was spread. Government control also meant other governments hesitated to do business with it. The British and the Americans, of course, are just as jealous of where sophisticated weapons like *Starstreak* are sold. (It was deployed with NATO forces in Kosovo in 1999, the opportunity being exploited for frequent test firings; but *Starstreak* was never used in anger. It was also deployed in the Gulf in 2003).

When he retired to West Sussex in 2002, Terry Stone forecast another great half-century for Thales Air Defence and was willing to speculate that Castlereagh had the talent to become a centre of excellence in the field, not only for the United Kingdom, but on the world stage as well. Indeed the omens are good politically. Thales as

Starstreak on deployment in Kosovo
in support of the UN Forces

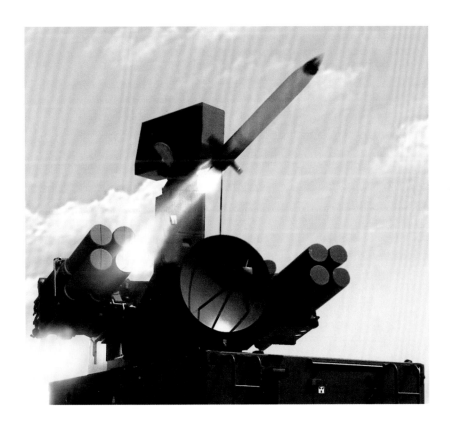

The *VT1* missile manufactured by
Thales Air Defence to equip the
Crotale air defence system

a whole has been taking on orders at the record rate of 11bn. euros a year, the fruit of being able to command nearly one fifth of the annual French defence equipment budget. President Chirac's ambitious new five-year programme to upgrade the French armed forces means that even higher sales can be expected. The French Government, of course, also profits from this business through its reduced 32.6 per cent. shareholding in Thales; although the trend is towards further privatisation.

The financial strength provided by this base is vital to the ability of Thales Air Defence to fund the research and development essential to its future. Cash-strapped governments look more and more to industry to finance this unaided. The result is mounting pressure to merge across national frontiers.

Millar Crawford, absent for four years during which he oversaw the start-up of a new industrial plant south of Belfast, returned to Castlereagh as Terry Stone's successor in the autumn of 2002. He saw the vast discrepancy in the research and development budgets of the American industry vis-à-vis the European as the big challenge, threatening to create a situation where it would always be simpler for Europe to buy an American product off the shelf –

> When you look at the ratios of spend in R and D per serviceman, the US is way out there in a factor times Europe. Now the UK is right up at number one within Europe. But there's still a factor of difference with the US. That's why a small missile systems division wouldn't have survived or been viable. We wouldn't have the political clout, the leverage or the financial support to be able to keep playing at the top table.[6]

As for Castlereagh, its involvement in the first division of the defence business puts a new premium on the obligation to think big. That means thinking internationally. When Terry Stone arrived in Northern Ireland in 1984, he was appalled to find that the engineers at Castlereagh had not talked to their principal competitors - Matra at Villacoublay – for twenty years. He nailed that brand of isolationism as the death knell of the enterprise essential to the survival of Castlereagh. It is largely due to Stone's leadership that the team at the plant is now every bit as internationally conscious as its former associates, the other components of Shorts, were always obliged to be. In this evolution, the issue of ownership and nationality has become much less focussed. The new BAE Systems corporate title lost the old British label. Thales is now much less exclusively French than its Thomson-CSF parent used to be. Thales now has a British headquarters at Weybridge and a UK head in Alex Dorrian.

Its branch at Castlereagh passed its fiftieth birthday with a much smaller staff than formerly: about 600. But some 230 of those are qualified engineers; and in 2001, Thales Air Defence at Castlereagh was the most profitable of the five companies responsible for the thirteen Thales operating centres in the United Kingdom.[7]

In the same year, as it happened, Castlereagh opened negotiations with Saab-Bofors of Sweden to jointly tender for a new weapons requirement for anti-armour missiles for the Ministry of Defence. The joint tender having succeeded, a formal contract was signed in January 2003. The MBT-LAW missile, fired from the shoulder, will be assembled solely at Crossgar – for the British and Swedish armies in the first instance, but with much wider sales potential. Hugh Conway's inspiration of the early 1950s, that the rewards would go to the engineers who developed a fast modern weapon like *Seacat* to replace the 40mm Bofors gun, had come full circle.

The Main Battle Tank Light Anti-Tank Weapon, designed by Saab Bofors, was selected by the UK Ministry of Defence to satisfy its light anti-tank requirements

NOTES

1   Terry Stone, interview with author

2   Millar Crawford, do

3   David Beatty, do

4   Crawford, do

5   Beatty, do.

6   Crawford, interview with author

7   Irish Times, 12 October 2001; Financial Times, 13 September 2002

Glossary

Analogue computer	A computer which uses physical quantities such as voltages, weight, etc to represent numbers
GLTV	Green Light Test Vehicle
GPV	General Purpose Vehicle
Gyroscope	Rotating wheel which maintains a fixed direction while turning on a free axis
HTP	Hydrogen Test Peroxide, used as a rocket fuel
HVM	High Velocity Missile
Mach 1	Speed of sound – 680 mph
MI5	Military Intelligence, Department 5, the British Security Service, under Foreign Office control and dealing with internal subversion.
MI6	Military Intelligence, Department 6, the Secret Intelligence Service, under Foreign Office control and in charge of British espionage abroad
NASA	National Aeronautical and Space Administration (USA)
Polaris	American submarine-launched, long-range, nuclear missile with a velocity of Mach 10
RAE	Royal Aircraft Establishment, Farnborough, Hants
RPE	Rocket Propulsion Establishment, Westcott, near Oxford
SAS/SBS	Special Air Service, founded by David Stirling of the Scots Guards in the Western Desert in 1941 as a long-range commando force, trained to attack targets behind enemy lines. The Special Boat Service offered a marine arm.

SD330	Shorts' commuter airliner, also adaptable for freight, which made its maiden flight in 1974 and entered airline service in 1976
Skyvan	Shorts' smaller, freight workhorse, precursor of the 330, and launched in 1963
Telemetry	Means of transmitting readings from an instrument to a distant receiver, as from those in a test missile relayed to the launching point
V1	German Second World War unmanned flying bomb
V2	German Second World War high-altitude, rocket-propelled bomb
VTOL	Vertical Take-off and Land

Index